THINGS
to Make and Do

By

ESTHER M. BJOLAND

1961
STANDARD EDUCATION SOCIETY, INC.
CHICAGO

ACKNOWLEDGMENTS

Grateful acknowledgment is herewith made for design, illustration, and typography to the following: American Typesetting Corporation, Donald Brown as Art Director, and Virginia G. Atkins, Mary Cinefro, Douglas Graves, Frank Johnson, Mel Schultz, artists.

FOREWORD

Toys are important to a child but too many of them can be a handicap. A child who has a chest full of ready-made playthings often becomes indifferent to them. Eventually none amuse or please and the toy-owner becomes restless, dissatisfied, and frequently difficult to live with. Such a child urgently needs a wholesome release from his ready-made toys and an opportunity to make some of his own.

It is natural for every child to want to make things, to experiment, to explore. He should be permitted to try to create with his hands that which he sees in his mind's eye. No child ever should be denied this freedom of expression.

In this book are 146 projects for which the cost of materials is little or nothing. Many of the activities can be done in several ways. Because they are not merely "busy work" projects but mediums of expression, the possibilities of **Things To Make and Do** are almost endless. The widest variety of activities has been selected both to provide something for every mood and occasion and also to encourage children to express themselves according to their individual experiences and thinking. It is intended to assist the truly creative child to see beyond the obvious and create from his own imagination.

In so far as possible, each child should find out for himself how to handle a brush, how to mix paints, how to cut, how to carve. He should be permitted to select an activity according to his own level of ability and to go forward at his own rate of speed.

It is the experience in using the hands and in the process of creating that is of vital importance to a child's growth. If parents and teachers will be on the alert to give encouragement and help, when needed, they will experience the joy and satisfaction that comes from seeing their children or their pupils express their creative urges with hammer and nails, knife and chisel, paint and crayons, needles and thread, paper and cloth—simple materials, tools, and equipment within the reach of every home and school.

Esther M. Bjoland

TABLE OF CONTENTS

A CIRCUS PARADE

It's great fun to create a circus parade out of different-sized corks, thin wire, bits of yarn, felt, cloth, toothpicks, and a few feathers. It's easy, too! Just study the sketches found on this page. Notice how the corks are held together with wire, how the elephant's tail is made from a bit of braided wire, how the tail of the giraffe is made from a piece of brown darning cotton, how the tail of the ostrich is fashioned from feathers, and how the ears of the elephant are made from felt.

Once you have made the animals shown here you and your friends will be eager to make others to join your circus parade of cork animals.

9

A milkman needs a milk wagon. To make his wagon use boxes, spools, heavy string, and cardboard.

A milkman needs bottles. Cut them from white cardboard.

FOLD UNDER →

A milkman also needs a basket in which to carry the milk bottles. Use a match box for the basket and attach strings to it in this manner to make its handle.

10

Play Milkman

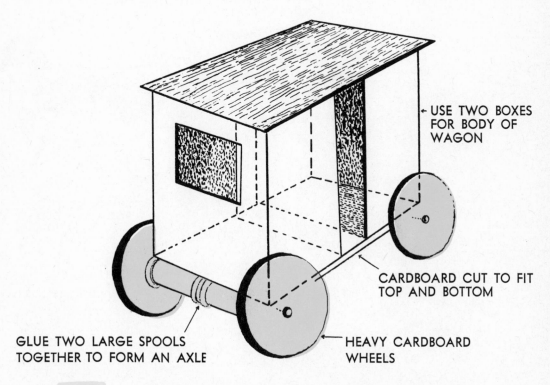

← USE TWO BOXES FOR BODY OF WAGON

CARDBOARD CUT TO FIT TOP AND BOTTOM

GLUE TWO LARGE SPOOLS TOGETHER TO FORM AN AXLE

HEAVY CARDBOARD WHEELS

A milkman needs money to make change. Make the money from cardboard like this—

5¢   10¢   25¢

If you wish, you can use tiny bottles instead of the cardboard ones.

PICTURES ANY CHILD CAN MAKE

Cut circles, triangles, and rectangles from different colored papers. Arrange these shapes to make pictures like this one.

Then paste them in position on a piece of heavy cardboard.

To draw the circles a circle maker can be made in this manner from stiff manila paper.

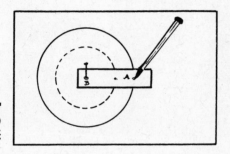

INSERT PENCIL AT "A" PUT PIN "B" AT DESIRED DISTANCE FROM "A" AND SWING PENCIL TO MAKE A CIRCLE

FLOATING

Trace Fig. I on lightweight cardboard. Cut out your drawings. Use an orange crayon to color the duck a light orange.

From 1½ inch cork cut away a section to flatten it. Fig. 2. On the opposite side cut a slit. Glue the duck into the slit. Then set it afloat in the bath tub when you are taking your bath.

Fig. I

Fig. 2

oys

Fig. 3

Trace Fig. 3 on white paper. Cut out. Use your pattern to make 2 copies of it on glazed paper. Paste together with the exception of the flap marked AB. Spread flaps apart at the dotted lines.

Obtain a Dixie-cup top or Dutch-cheese box top. To make it water proof color both sides heavily with crayons.

Paste these flaps onto the cup or box top and set the swan afloat in the bath tub.

For this fun cut a number of circles from colored paper.

Then change them into umbrellas like th

RAINY
DAY FUN

16

Cut out the umbrellas. Then from magazine pictures cut out pictures of boys and girls.

Put these boys and girls under the umbrellas.

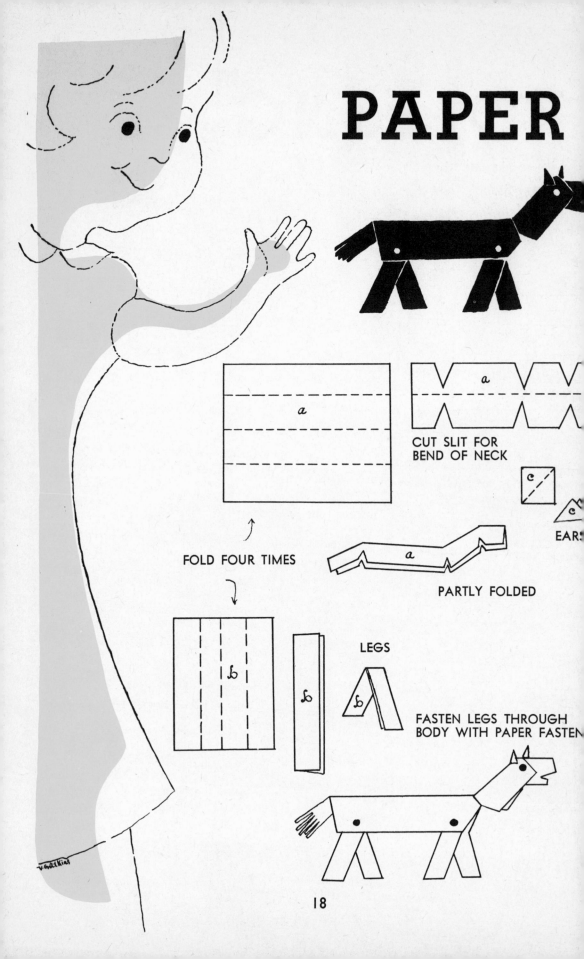

PAPER

CUT SLIT FOR
BEND OF NECK

a

EARS

FOLD FOUR TIMES

PARTLY FOLDED

a

LEGS

FASTEN LEGS THROUGH
BODY WITH PAPER FASTEN

b

FOLDING

Little folks can have many happy times
making things from folded paper such
as the man and the horse.

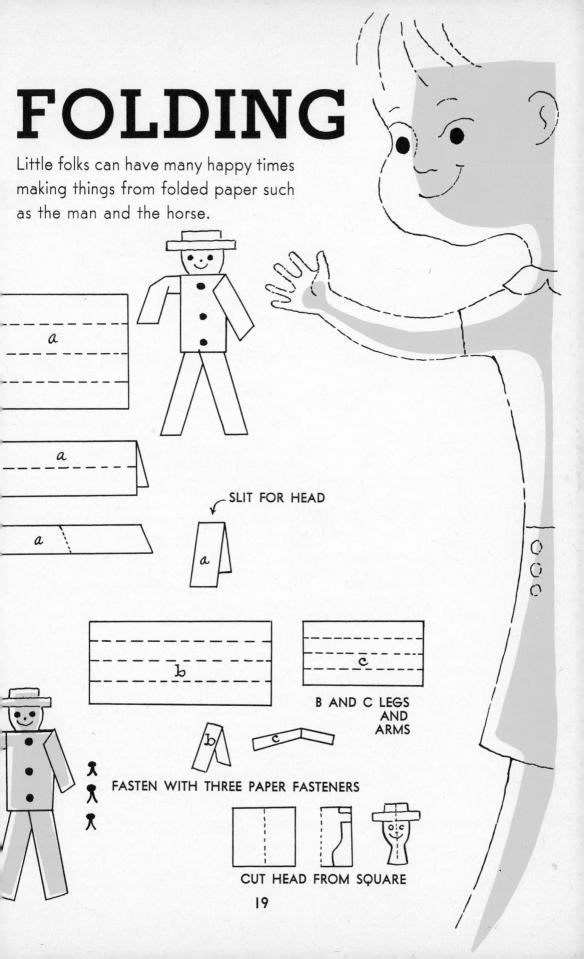

a

a

a

SLIT FOR HEAD

a

b

c

B AND C LEGS
AND
ARMS

b   c

FASTEN WITH THREE PAPER FASTENERS

CUT HEAD FROM SQUARE

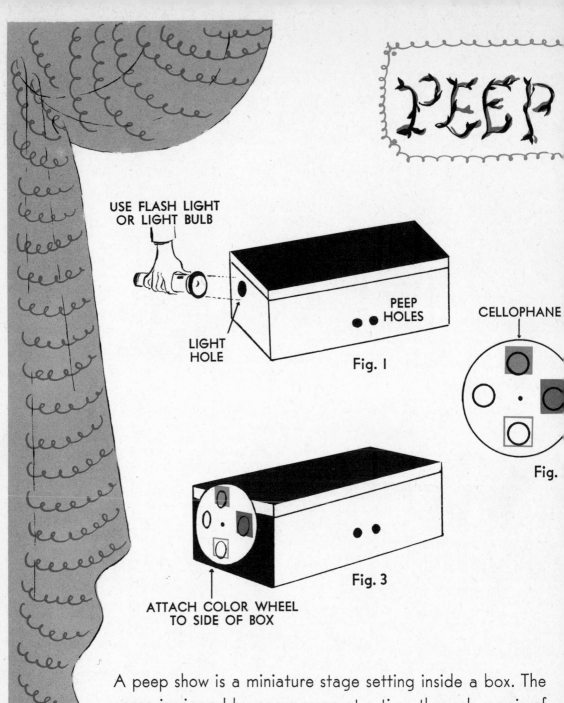

USE FLASH LIGHT
OR LIGHT BULB

PEEP
HOLES

CELLOPHANE

LIGHT
HOLE

Fig. I

Fig.

Fig. 3

ATTACH COLOR WHEEL
TO SIDE OF BOX

PEEP

A peep show is a miniature stage setting inside a box. The scene is viewed by one person at a time through a pair of peep holes. Fig. I.

In order to let the one-person-audience see the show there must be an opening through which light can fall upon the stage setting. Fig. I. To add beauty to the scene make a color wheel. Fig. 2. Attach to the side of the box so that it may be rotated over the light hole. Fig. 3.

SHOW

BACK OF
CABIN

LIGHT HOLE

BEND UNDER
FOR SUPPORT

Line the inside of the box with paper, the color of which is appropriate for the scene. Use toy dolls and animals to represent characters, or small pictures of animals and persons cut from magazines and mounted upon cardboard bases, such as the Pilgrim figure shown here.

Scenes from other lands, from favorite stories, or from history make excellent stage settings for peep shows. The one given here depicts the Pilgrims going to church.

Cork Bracelet

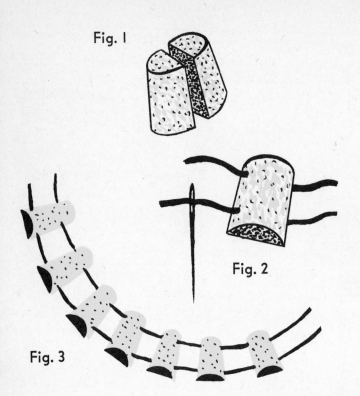

Fig. 1

Fig. 2

Fig. 3

Cut all the corks in half. Fig. 1 Use a greased knife blade to do this. It will make the cutting an easy process. Then thread the cork sections on gaily colored string. Fig. 2. Use two threaded needles. Pass each one through a cork before adding a second cork to the string. Fig. 3. Tie the ends of the two strings together in a pretty knot.

Cardboard Jewelry

Cut diamond-shaped figures from pieces of colored construction paper. Fig. 1. Double and paste over a string of yarn. Fig. 2. Tie to form a necklace. Cut cardboard in the shape of squares, rectangles, and the like. Lace together with yarn or string in the manner seen here. If you do not possess a paper punch use a darning needle to make the holes.

Fig. 1   Fig. 2

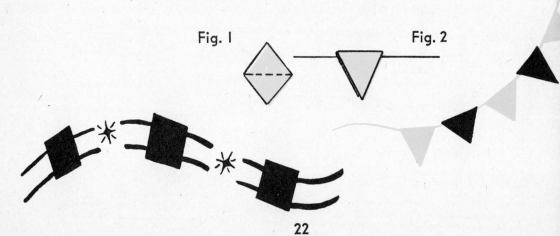

To make this parasol you will need a cork ¾ of an inch in diameter, 8 toothpicks, a long wire pin with a bead head, and colored yarn.

Cut the cork to form a section ½ inch in thickness. Into it insert 8 toothpicks at equal distances from each other. Fig. 1. Fasten a piece of colored yarn to one of the toothpick-ribs making this fastening close to the cork. Begin weaving in and out among the toothpicks until you have made a pretty covering. Fasten the end of the thread about one of the toothpick ribs, Fig. 2. Insert a long wire pin with a beadlike head into the center of the underside of the cork to form the parasol rod with a decorative handle. A short wire hairpin can be substituted for the long wire pin. Bend one end of the hairpin to form the handle. Fig. 3.

A Cork Parasol for a Wee Doll

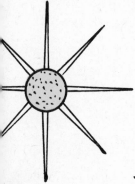

Fig. 1

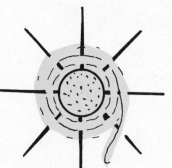

Fig. 2

Fig. 3

Colored Paper Doilies

Obtain a supply of white paper lace doilies like the one shown here and a box of crayons.

Spread the doily flat upon a table, study its design, then proceed to color its border and the flowers within the border with different colors of crayons.

Use colored doilies to decorate paper plates or as a background for pictures.

Color
This Redheaded Woodpecker

On this page is a picture of a red-headed woodpecker and an outline drawing of the same bird.

Make a copy of the outline drawing of the woodpecker. Then color it. Use the colored picture as a guide.

A SPOOL RACK

Mother will welcome a spool rack for her sewing room. Get a breadboard, preferably one that is no longer in use. A coat of paint will make it as attractive as a new one. Be sure the board is clean before painting it. When the paint is dry, add a small decalcomania at the top and bottom of the board. Then space

Fig. 1

evenly the nails which are to serve as holders for the spools. Use a pretty matching ribbon for a hanger. Fig. 1.

If a plain breadboard is not available, use an evenly cut piece of board. Paint this board. Then space evenly upon it the nails

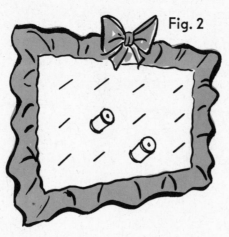

Fig. 2

which are to hold the spools of thread. With thumbtacks tack on a ruffle around the board. Use a large bow to hang the spool rack on a wall of the sewing room or a closet door. Fig. 2.

BOOK ENDS FROM TIN CANS

Select 2 tin fruit cans whose tops have been removed with a key-type can opener. Remove labels and thoroughly wash the cans. Paint inside and out. When paint is dry, add an attractive cut-out picture from a magazine. Glue in place. Shellac over the cut-out picture, smoothing it into place. Allow to dry.

Fill the cans with white sand. Add a tiny dime-store evergreen tree if the cans have been painted green and decorated with a Christmas scene.

A PICTURE HOLDER

If you are looking for something to give Mother for her desk, a picture holder like the one shown here is certain to please. To make it follow the sketches and directions given here.

Fig. I

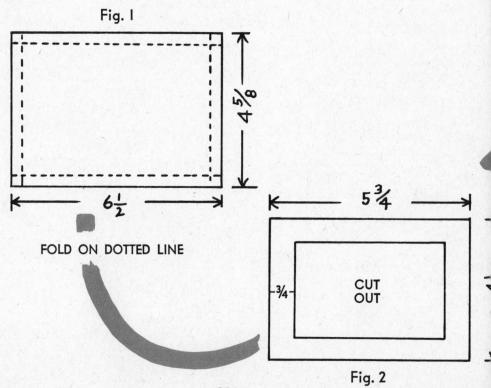

4 5/8

6 1/2

FOLD ON DOTTED LINE

5 3/4

3/4

CUT
OUT

Fig. 2

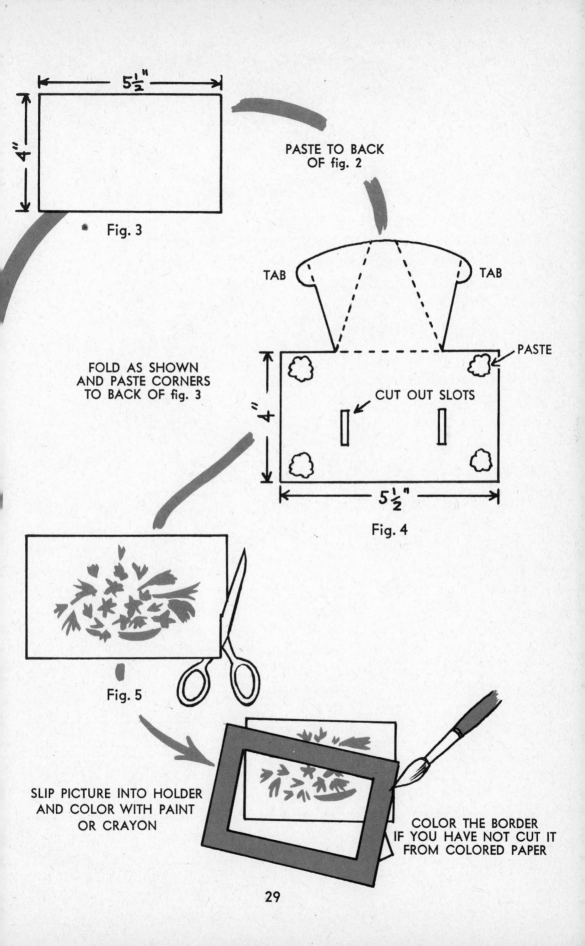

5½"

4"

Fig. 3

PASTE TO BACK
OF fig. 2

TAB   TAB

PASTE

FOLD AS SHOWN
AND PASTE CORNERS
TO BACK OF fig. 3

CUT OUT SLOTS

4"

5½"

Fig. 4

Fig. 5

SLIP PICTURE INTO HOLDER
AND COLOR WITH PAINT
OR CRAYON

COLOR THE BORDER
IF YOU HAVE NOT CUT IT
FROM COLORED PAPER

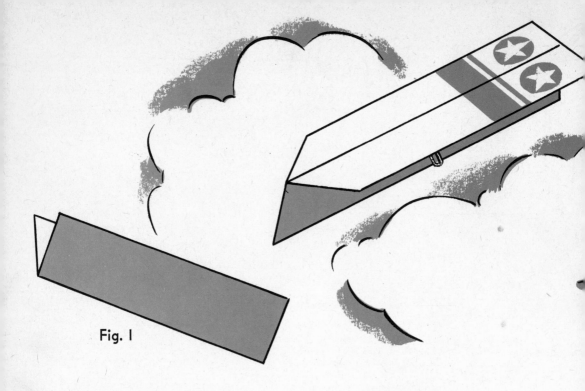

Fig. I

A GLIDER

Here is a very easy way to make a glider.

Fold a rectangular sheet of paper in half the long way. Fig. I.

Fold back the corner of one end of the paper. Then fold back the facing corner in just the same way. Notice how these corner folds match. Fig. 2.

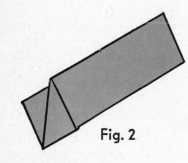

Fig. 2

Now fold down the entire length of both sides of the glider to make its wings. Fig. 3.

Spread the wings of the glider. Use 2 paper clips to fasten the plane together. Fig. 3. The weight of the paper clips will make your plane glide smoothly through the air.

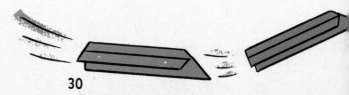

Fig. 3

A PARACHUTE

It's fun to make a parachute and more fun to see it float downward as a real parachute does. It's easy to make, too. Ask mother for a paper napkin, then find 4 lengths of string each 12 inches long and a small cork. Tie a piece of string to each of the 4 corners of the napkin. Then tie the loose ends of the strings around the cork.

Find a chair, stand on it, hold the parachute by the middle of the top of the napkin, then drop it. Down, down it will float to the floor.

A ROLY-POLY
FOR BABY

Obtain an oatmeal box. Punch holes in bottom and cover. Pull a string through these holes. Fill the box with 24 dried beans or buttons. Paste the cover in place. Use Scotch tape or adhesive tape to seal the cover in place. Tie the ends of the string.

The roly-poly may be made attractive with a covering of pretty paper or with a coat of paint.

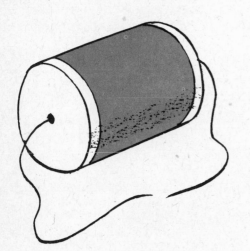

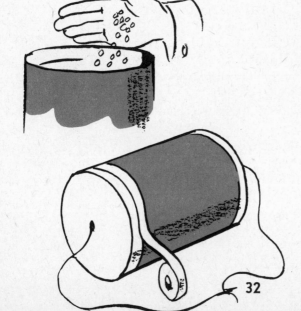

RING A RING

Cut ½ inch rings from a paper towel tube. Wind each with white or colored yarn. Fig. 1.

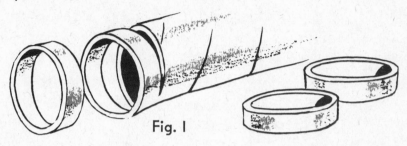

Fig. 1

Cut from the end piece of an orange crate a 4 inch square. Bore a hole in its center and fit within it an 8 or 10 inch dowel stick. Glue in place. Fig. 2.

Fig. 2

A very little child will like to pile the rings on to the dowel stick. Older children will like to toss the rings over it.

FUN WITH SPOOLS

It is easy to make a clown doll and a dog from spools, wire, and beads. Always knot wire at ends to prevent the toys from falling apart. Paint, varnish, or shellac the spools.

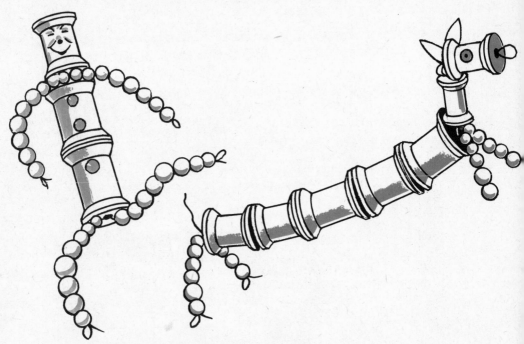

To make spool bookends use 5 large spools. Saw each in half. Glue 5 of the cut parts onto a block of wood. Fig. 1. Do the same with the remaining spool sections. Paint, decorate, and shellac.

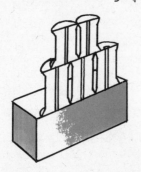

Fig. 1

To make a candlestick holder use 2 spools. Cut each in half. Put together as in Fig. 1. Cut base from thin wood. Use small nails, driven through the bottom of base, or glue to fasten spool sections to the base. Paint, decorate, and shellac.

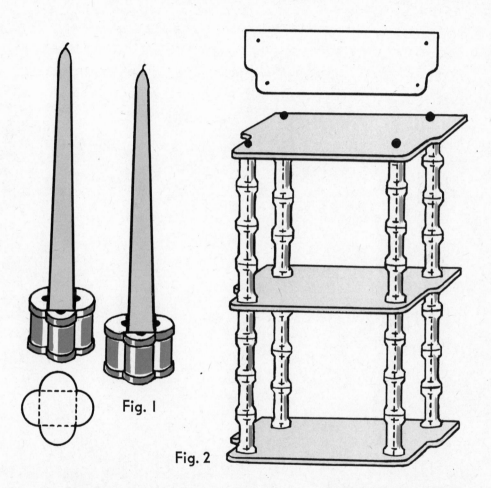

Fig. 1

Fig. 2

To make the hanging shelf obtain 48 spools of the same size. Use 4 between each pair of shelves at each of the 4 corners. Use 4 little spools at the corners of the lower top shelves to give the hanging shelf a finished appearance.

Cut the shelves from thin wood and bore holes in the corners of each. Then pass pieces of stiff wire or heavy cord through these holes and the spools. Knot wire or cord at top and bottom to hold spools and shelves in place. Fig. 2.

Select a large box with a deep cover. Remove 2 sides of cover to make it fit inside the box. Replace cut-down sides with Scotch tape. Fig. 1.

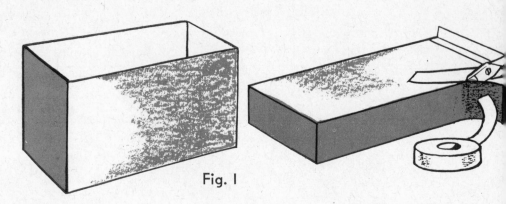

Fig. 1

Punch 6 holes in the remodeled cover to hold the ice-cream cones. Fig. 2.

Cut 4 wheels from heavy card-board. Fasten to box with two-pronged paper fasteners. Attach a pipe cleaner handle. Fig. 3.

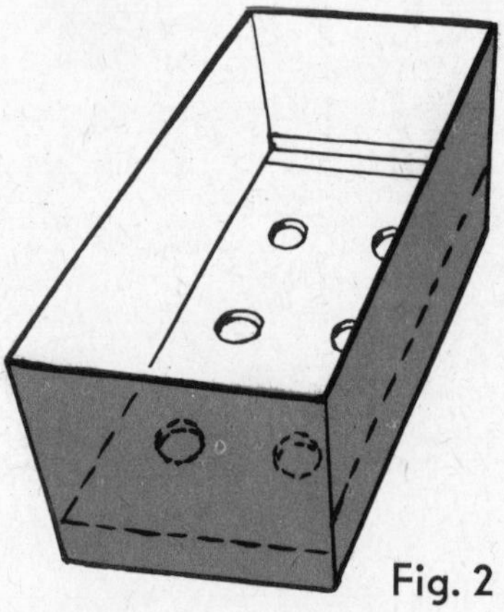

Fig. 2

Fig. 3

Fashion a piece of cardboard to fit top of cart. Cut this fitted-piece in two and hinge parts with tape. Fig. 4. Fasten the lid. Add a tiny bell and a gay-colored umbrella. Fig. 5.

Fig. 4

Fig. 5

Make 6 ice-cream cones. Fig. 6. Fill each with a bit of cotton. Place in cover. Put lid down. You are now ready to sell ice-cream cones to your friends.

Fig. 6

A LEAN-TO

A lean-to, the kind some of the early pioneers built, makes an excellent temporary shelter. To erect one drive 2 poles upright in the ground to the height desired for the front of the lean-to. Make the distance between them the desired width of your shelter. Fasten securely a third pole across the top of the 2 upright poles. Fig. 1.

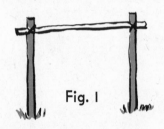

Fig. 1

Next cut a number of long poles for the roof. Lay these between the 2 uprights with one end of each pole extending a short distance beyond the cross bar and the other end resting on the ground. Lash small poles between the sides of the roof and the upright. Cover top and sides with bark or tarpaper or canvas. Hang cheesecloth or a blanket, depending upon the weather, for a doorway to your lean-to.

GRASS HUTS

Grass huts are fun to make. But every boy knows that after the grass has become dry, he must not have any fire near his hut.

To make such a hut—

Cut 9 or 10 poles measuring 2" in diameter and 9 feet long. Draw an 8 foot circle on the ground. Drive the poles about 1 foot into the ground at equal distances around the circle. Pull the tops together with strong rope. Then bind small branches around the poles, keeping them parallel to the ground and about 1 foot above each other. Fig. 1. Do not forget to leave a space for the entrance.

Cut a large amount of long grass such as marsh grass. Fold small bunches of this grass in the center over the circle of branches bound to the poles of the framework. Begin this folding at the bottom of the framework.

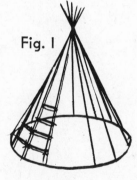

Fig. 1

Thereafter fold each row of grass to overlap the row below it. Fig. 2.

Fig. 2

A SKYSCRAPER

To build a skyscraper select 7 boxes of different sizes. Draw windows in each and pile one upon the other. For very little folks it's great fun to build a towering house and great fun to knock it down, only to rebuild it.

A PUSSY WILLOW PICTURE

Large fluffy pussy willows make fine pussy cats if they are pressed very lightly and pasted to paper.

To make a pussy willow picture paint a scene with a fence or the branch of a tree upon which the cats can sit.

Place the pussy willows in place. Mark this place. Then paint the heads and tails of the cats. When the paint is dry, paste the pussy willows on the paper to make the bodies of the cats.

Flowers cut from paper may be added to give more color to the picture.

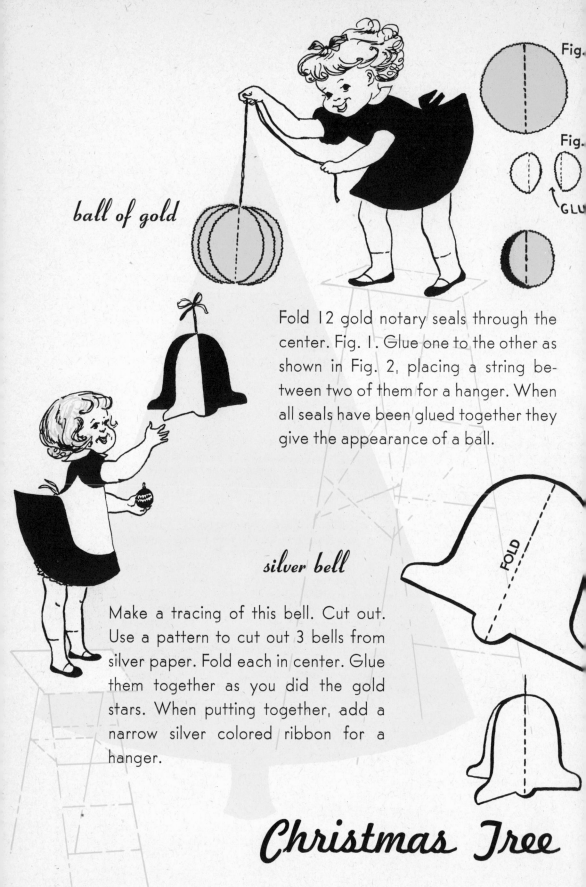

ball of gold

Fold 12 gold notary seals through the center. Fig. 1. Glue one to the other as shown in Fig. 2, placing a string between two of them for a hanger. When all seals have been glued together they give the appearance of a ball.

silver bell

Make a tracing of this bell. Cut out. Use a pattern to cut out 3 bells from silver paper. Fold each in center. Glue them together as you did the gold stars. When putting together, add a narrow silver colored ribbon for a hanger.

Fig.

Fig.

GLU

FOLD

Christmas Tree

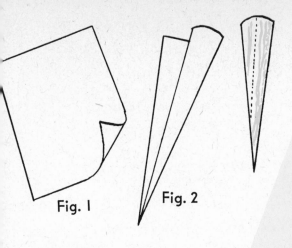

Fig. 1   Fig. 2

icicle

Cut a piece of cellophane to measure 9 inches by $2\frac{1}{2}$ inches. Begin rolling the strip at the lower right hand corner. Fig. 1, and continue rolling until it appears as Fig. 2. Paste top end with Scotch tape. Use colored threads to attach icicles to Christmas tree.

gold star

Fold 3 large gummed stars in half. Glue together as you did the notary seals. Attach a loop of narrow yellow ribbon between 2 of them to make a hanger. Fig. 1.

FOLD

Fig. 1

Ornaments

EASTER EGG FUN

Decorating Easter eggs is one of the "pleasantest things ever a child can do."

Begin the fun by making —

chicken on the nest

Select an egg that will fit a nut cup. Hard boil and cool. Cut a chicken head from yellow crepe paper. Cut it double and with the grain of the paper. Stuff a little cotton inside the head to fill it out. Fig. 1. Paste in place on the egg. Then cut two wings and a tail from the yellow crepe paper. Fig. 2. Paste in place. Make a comb from red crepe paper. Fig. 3. Paste in place on the egg. Fill the nut cup with small colored candied eggs. Then set the hen on the nest. Fig. 4.

PASTE

Fig. 2

Fig. 3

PASTE

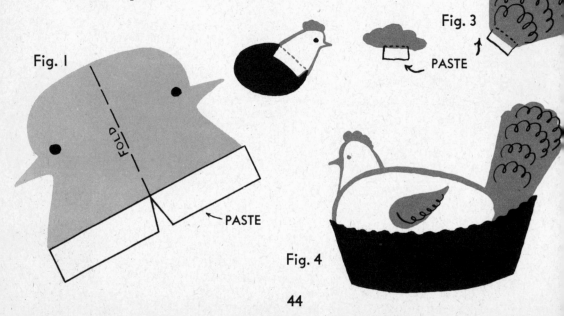

Fig. 1

FOLD

PASTE

Fig. 4

A Happy Easter Egg

Before dipping a large white egg in dye write upon it with melted tallow or paraffin the words "A Happy Easter." The dye will not color the waxed letters. After the dye bath, remove the paraffin. The words will stand out in clear white on the dyed egg. Use the same method to make a picture on an egg.

Surprise Easter Eggs

You can have a great deal of fun creating different egg characters for each member of your family. Place each in a paper nut cup that wears a fluted ruffle.

To make these surprise Easter eggs use ink, paint, pieces of lace, tissue paper, bits of cloth, and lace paper doilies.

The pictures here will show you how easy it is to make these egg characters—

Huck Finn

Jolly Sailor

Pretty Lady

Father

Baby Sister

45

Fig.

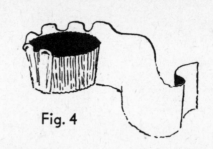
Fig. 4

FLOWER BASKET PARTY FAVORS

Line a lace doily in the manner shown in Fig. 1. Wrap a pipe cleaner with narrow ribbon. Roll the doily upward and attach ribboned pipe cleaner to make the basket handle. Fig. 2.

Silver or colored foils, such as that used by florists to wrap flower pots, make excellent linings, especially if you wish to fill the basket with flowers, such as, violets or crocuses, which have had their stems wrapped in wads of moistened cotton to keep them from wilting.

A nut cup makes an excellent foundation for a flower basket. Cut flower petals from crepe paper. Fig. 3. Paste on the cup as shown in Fig. 4. Ruffle edges. Attach a pipe cleaner handle. Fig. 5.

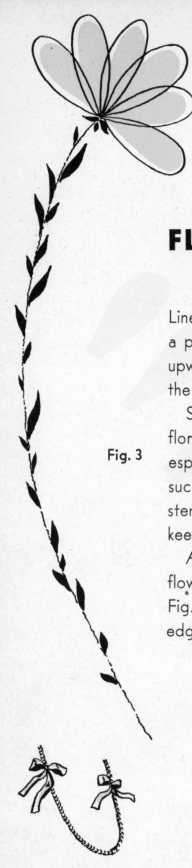
Fig. 3

Fig. 1

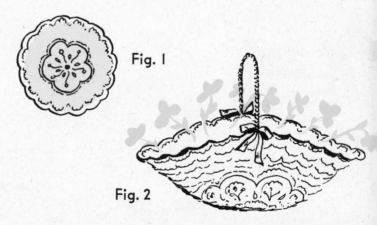
Fig. 2

A CAN RATTLE FOR HALLOWEEN

Obtain at least 3 large tin cans each having a removable lid. Punch a hole in the center of the bottom of each and in the center of each lid. These holes should be large enough to permit the passage of a rope through them. The rope should be of clothesline thickness and about 5 feet in length. String the cans and their lids on the rope one at a time. To hold each can in place tie a knot outside the bottom of each one. After the cans have been strung in place put a handful of small pebbles in each can and clamp the covers in place. Hang the rattle on a porch beam. Each time a guest arrives grasp the tail end of the rope and shake the can rattle to announce his arrival to the other guests.

PAPER POTTERY

Obtain several rolls of serpentine crepe paper, each one a different color. Select a roll. Rewind it very, very tightly. To start the rewinding, fold 2 inches of the paper back upon itself to provide extra thickness. Fig. 1. When you reach the end of the roll, select another roll of a different color. Glue the ends of the two rolls together by putting a dab of paste on the roll under the loose end and press the end down. Then place a second dab of paste on top and start the next colored streamer. Fig. 2. Continue winding. Each new color is added in the same manner. Continue until you have a disk with a diameter large enough on which to set a hot dish. Fig. 3. Glue the tail of the last roll to the roll itself. Shellac the hotplate pad.

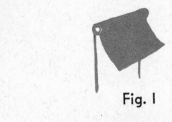

Fig. 1

Fig. 2

To make a bowl, wind a disk to measure from 4 to 5 inches in diameter. After the winding has been completed, hold the disk in one hand, carefully curve the sides with the thumb of one hand, keeping the bottom flat. Fig. 4. It is at this point that you may come to grief if the winding has not been tight.

Fig. 3

After you are satisfied with the shape of the bowl give it 3 coats of white shellac. Allow each coat to dry before another is added. Finish the bowl with 2 coats of very good waterproof varnish or shellac.

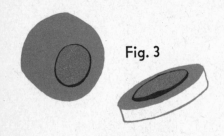

Fig. 4

48

Fig. 1

JIG SAW PUZZLE

From a magazine cut out a pretty picture. Paste it on a piece of cardboard. Fig. 1. When dry, use a pencil and a ruler to mark the picture into odd shapes. Draw these lines very lightly. Fig. 2. Then with the ruler laid along these lines go over them with a single-edged razor or a knife until you have cut through the cardboard. Do not try to cut through the heavy paper with the first stroke. Such a cutting will leave jagged edges.

Put the pieces into a box. Wrap as a birthday gift for your best friend.

Fig. 2

49

PAPER SNOWFLAKES

Paper snowflakes make beautiful ornaments on a Christmas tree. They may be made of light yellow, silver, gold, or white paper. Three thicknesses of tissue paper make effective snowflakes.

Obtain a square of paper. Fold it in the center, then again in halves. This will divide the paper into fourths. Fig. 1. Fold the quarter into 2 thirds. Fig. 2. Then sketch the outline of a snowflake as shown in Fig. 3. Open. Instead of sketching an outline you may cut free hand the outline of a star. Make narrow slashes all around the outside to give the star a light airy look. String the snowflakes on a very fine thread. Hang on the branches of the tree.

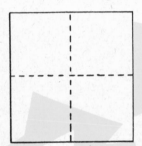

Fig. 1

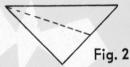

Fig. 2

Fig. 3

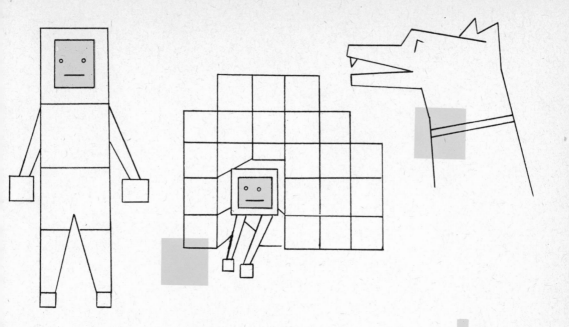

FUN WITH SQUARES
AND STRAIGHT LINES

Begin the fun by making copies of the figures on this page. Then start making queer pictures of your own.

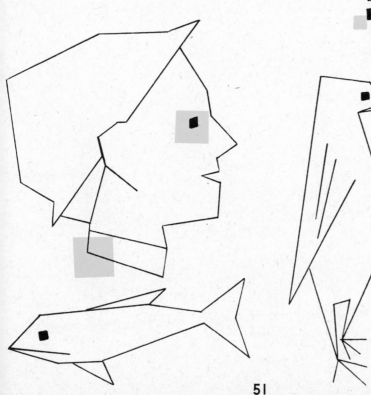

Vegetable dolls make interesting table decorations and prizes. They are simple to make.

The Pony — Obtain a large cucumber. Fashion his ears from corn husks, his legs and neck from carrots, his mane and tail from corn silk, and his mouth and nostrils from black paper cut to shape. Use stiff wire to hold his body together.

The Turkey—Obtain a Hubbard squash for the body. Retain stem for the neck. Use stiff wire to fasten a carrot head to the neck and carpet tacks to fasten the white paper eyes. Use hair pins to fasten the cabbage tail and wings. Attach the beard of grass with a tack and the asparagus berries and white beans to the neck with pins. Attach cabbage stalks and their roots with wire. Run a long stiff wire through the body down into holes made in a board which is to serve as a base for the figure.

Susannah and Sam — Use small watermelons to make the bodies of these dolls. Use small squashes for their heads and corn silk for their hair. Wire in place. Attach black watermelon seed eyes with small pins. Fashion their mouths from white paper. Pin in place. Use black beans for noses, potatoes for Sam's shoes on his corn legs, and cornhusks for Susannah's shoes on her corn legs. Attach with wire and strong pins. Fashion a bonnet for Susannah and a cap for Sam from corn-husks.

The Elephant — Obtain a pumpkin for the body. Attach a parsnip head to the body with a skewer. Make the ears of cabbage leaves and attach with hair pins. Use a wire nail to hold a parsnip tail in place. Fashion the tusks from parsnip and fasten with wire. Use firm wire to run through the legs made of corn up into the pumpkin body and then down into holes in a base of wood.

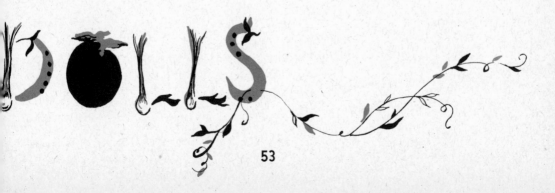

A Wall Pocket

CUT IN HALF

Fig. I

Obtain 2 paper plates, the 8 inch size. Cut one plate in half. Face the hollow parts of the plates toward each other. Mark places to punch holes for paper fasteners. Punch 2 small holes for a cord by which to hang this handy pocket on the wall.

You may lace the plates together with bright colored yarn, string, or cord. Fig. I. Also you may decorate the plates of the wall pocket by covering them with crepe paper, shellac, cloth, pictures from magazines, envelope linings, or household wax. Putting a coat of wax over all the decorated surfaces makes it easy to clean the wall pocket with a moistened cloth.

Whenever possible shellac the wall pocket. Use 2 coats of transparent shellac. Be sure the first coat is dry before the second one is applied.

Paper Plate Picture Frames

Select a round or a square paper plate. Paste a picture in the center of it. Cut a square or a circle of colored paper to fit around the picture. Paste in place and attach a hanger.

Cut a hole in the center of another plate, paint a band of color around the plate. When dry, paste the picture on from back of plate. Attach a hanger.

Cut a series of pictures from magazines. Paste them on individual plates. Fasten hangers on them. Select pictures appropriate to the place you want to use them.

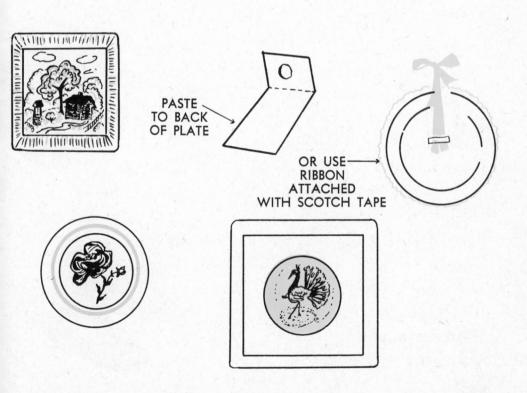

PASTE
TO BACK
OF PLATE

OR USE
RIBBON
ATTACHED
WITH SCOTCH TAPE

Fig. 1

DOLL'S HAT

Fig

Fig

Cut from stiff paper 2 brims as shown in Fig. 1.

Cut from tissue paper a crown. A lace paper doily may be used instead of the tissue paper. Gather the crown. Sew to the brim. Fig. 2.

Now place the second brim upon a lace paper doily. Cut out center to match the brim. Paste lace doily to brim. Fig. 3. Then attach it to the brim with the sewed crown. Fig. 4.

Add a flower for trimming and a narrow ribbon for ties.

Fig. 4

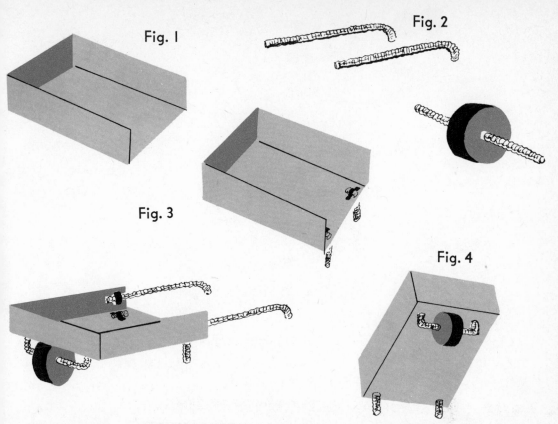

Fig. 1

Fig. 2

Fig. 3

Fig. 4

MATCH BOX WHEELBARROW

Cut one end from the tray of a match box in the manner shown in Fig. 1. Then cut 1 pipe cleaner in 2 equal parts, and a second pipe cleaner into 3 sections, 2 each $1\frac{1}{2}$ inches long, and the third section $3\frac{1}{2}$ inches long. Use the pipe cleaner halves for the handle of the wheelbarrow. Bend as shown in Fig. 2. Use the $1\frac{1}{2}$ inch pieces for legs and the $3\frac{1}{2}$ inch piece to attach the wheel to the wheelbarrow.

Insert legs in holes punched at the open end of the wheelbarrow and fasten with Scotch tape. Fig. 3.

Use a cork, cut to measure $\frac{7}{8}$ inch in diameter and about $\frac{1}{4}$ inch in thickness, for the wheel. Make a hole in its center. Run the $3\frac{1}{2}$ inch piece of pipe cleaner through it. Attach the pipe cleaner ends to the underside of the wheelbarrow with Scotch tape. Do likewise with the wheelbarrow handles. Fig. 4.

POTATO PRINTING

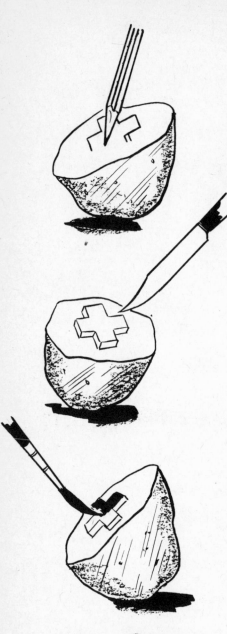

To make a potato block print slice a potato through the center. Find a design that will fit a cut surface. Draw or trace the design onto the potato, using a pencil or an orange stick. Pare away all parts of the surface that do not have any of the design on it. Cut to a depth of 1/4 inch.

Brush showcard paint across the raised design. Press it onto a sheet of paper, any kind, except glossy paper.

If ragged edges appear on the first imprints, cut away the uneven parts which may have been left in cutting the potato block print. Smudgy impressions will disappear after a few prints have been made.

To make an initial printing the block must be cut in reverse. This may be done by first drawing the letter as it should appear on a piece of paper. Then trace it on the reverse side by holding it up against a window pane. Cut this reverse pattern into the surface of the potato.

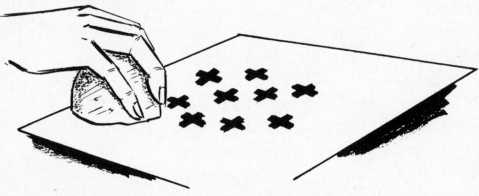

GLUE

MATCH BOX KNEE-HOLE DESK

Select 6 wooden match boxes. Stack 3 of them on top of each other. Glue them in place. Stack the remaining 3 boxes in the same way. Glue them in place.

Push the little drawers out. Make a small hole in the front of each through which to pass a two-pronged paper fastener. Bend back the prongs to make the tops serve as knobs for the drawers.

Paste a piece of cardboard across the 2 tiers of piled boxes to make a desk top. Cut a piece of a blotter to fit. Paste in place.

This desk may serve as a container for stamps, clips, or pins.

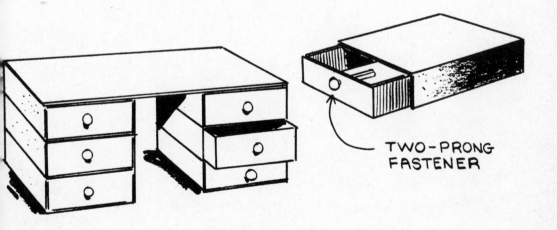

TWO-PRONG FASTENER

STICK PRINTING

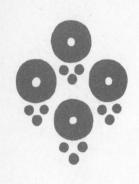

Interesting patterns or designs can be made with sticks, round, square, short, pointed, and odd shaped ones.

Dip the sticks into paint or ink or dye. Then press the painted ends onto paper to make designs such as seen here.

Instead of sticks you may use spools, dowels, blocks, nails, nuts, screws, clothespins, or meat skewers.

The heads of screws, which are flat circles with slots across them, make interesting marks when dipped in paint and printed on paper. Nuts will print squares with round holes or if turned on edge will create uniform rectangles. Nails can be used to make dots.

After you have become satisfied with your ability to create lovely designs on paper, you will enjoy arranging the same or other designs on a piece of cloth that is large enough to make a table runner. For printing the design use oil paints or printing ink. Both are color fast and will not disappear when the cloth is washed.

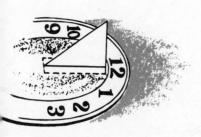
Fig. I

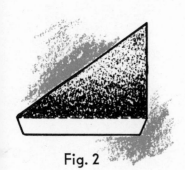
Fig. 2

Fig. 3

A SUN DIAL

To make a sun-dial get some stiff cardboard. From it cut a six inch square. With a compass draw on it the largest circle it will permit. Then draw a second circle $1/2$ inch inside the first one. Next mark off on the edge of the outer circle 12 equal places. Write the numbers from I to 12. Fig. I. Make a dot above each number to indicate the point at which the hours will change.

With a sharp pen knife cut a slot in the upper half of the dial's face. Begin the cut at the exact center, running the line to a point just below number 12. Make the slot as wide as the thickness of the cardboard. Then cut a piece of cardboard in the shape of a triangle. Fig. 2. Split its thickness in two from the bottom up to the dotted line. Bend the tabs up smoothly. Slip the triangular piece into the slot in the face of the dial. Glue the tabs and press them to the back of the dial. Fig. 3.

Place the finished dial in the sun with the back edge of the triangle pointing north. The sun will cause the triangle to cast a shadow upon the dial. If the shadow falls on 4 it is 4 o'clock. As the sun moves across the sky the shadow will change and move around the numbers on the dial.

Cut two propeller paddles of wood 1¼ inches square. Slip into each other. Fig. 1.

Cut 2 white cloth sails. Allow for a ¼ inch hem on all sides. Decorate with black cloth skull and bones. Fig. 2.

Cut the base of boat from cigar-box wood. Drill hole and glue wooden mast pole into it. Fig. 3.

Attach sails to mast and base of the boat. Fig. 4.

Slip elastic band over paddle, and over extensions A and B on base of boat. Twist paddle round and round on elastic. Fig. 4.

Set your boat for a sail to Treasure Island.

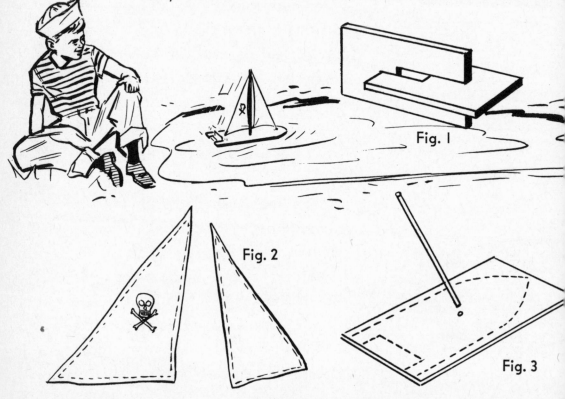

Fig. 1

Fig. 2

Fig. 3

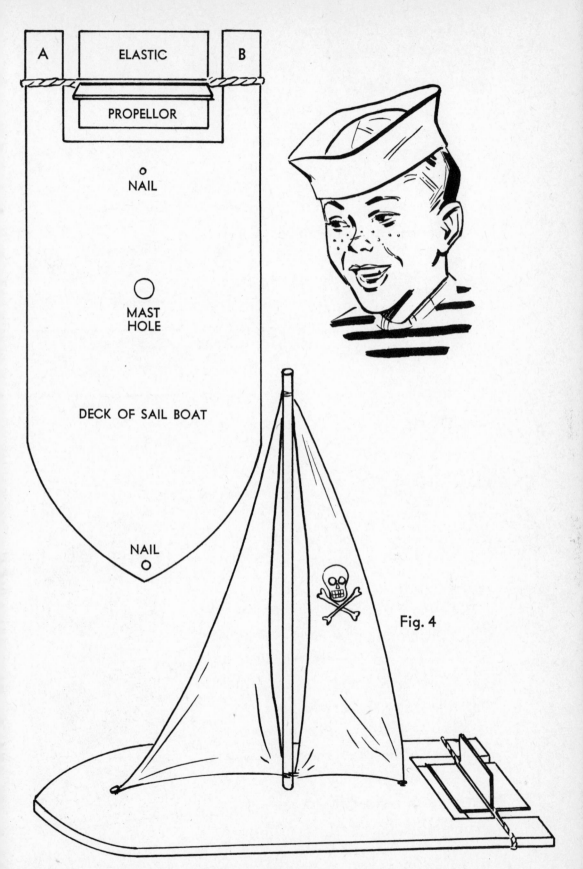

A

ELASTIC

B

PROPELLOR

o
NAIL

○
MAST
HOLE

DECK OF SAIL BOAT

NAIL
○

Fig. 4

BLOCK PRINTING

To make good linoleum block prints use a smooth grade of unlacquered linoleum which is light enough in color to make transfer lines, drawn in pencil, easily seen. Buy an extra piece on which to practice cutting deep straight lines at a slight angle.

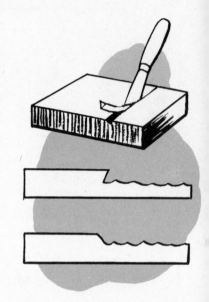

THE DESIGN

Because straight lines and large surfaces are most effective in linoleum prints, select a subject that will not require much detail.

Draw the design on paper the exact size of the block and place it in reverse on the block. To do this, rub oil over paper sketch to make it transparent. Rub the face with white chalk. Place face down on block. Trace with a pencil. Retrace the chalk lines with ink. In printing, the right hand side of block will become the left hand side of the completed print.

TOOLS

Although all block cutting may be done with a well sharpened knife, the most serviceable tool is the medium V-shaped veiner, Fig. I, which may be purchased for a small sum of money. Always cut away from the person and keep the hand which holds the block behind the direction of the cutting tool. The portion which is not to be printed may be cut away in large pieces. Cut the finer detail lines after all lines have been outlined with the knife. Round the outer edges of the block slightly after the cutting has been completed.

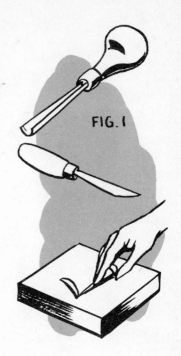

FIG. I

TAKING THE PROOF

Although the ink can be applied with a brush the results are not always as fine as when the ink is applied with a brayer, an instrument used for spreading ink. Fig. 2. Press some printing block ink, which comes in a tube, onto a piece of glass. Smooth it out with a side of a knife. Run the brayer back and forth over the glass until it is well inked. Then roll it over the surface of the block. Lay a piece of unglazed paper on top and with a smooth board press the paper against the linoleum. Or you may use an ordinary clothes wringer for a press. If the first proofs are not up to expectations, trim off the rough edges that remain on the block.

FIG. 2

Always clean the block with a soft rag and gasoline. Wrap in newspapers and keep in a dry place until you wish to use it again.

SHADOW PICTURES

Making shadow pictures is great fun. All you need is an electric light without a shade and a sheet.

To throw shadow pictures on the sheet you must have your hands between the light and the screen. And, of course, you must know the positions in which to place your hands and fingers in order to make interesting and convincing pictures on the screen.

In the sketches given here you will see a number of shadows of animals. Any boy or girl can make them after a little practice.

Once you have learned to make these various forms you will be able to move your fingers or thumbs so that the animals will seem alive. Much fun can be added to your show by imitating the sound of each animal as it parades across the screen.

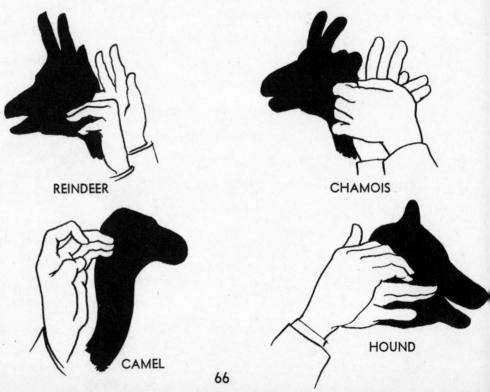

REINDEER

CHAMOIS

CAMEL

HOUND

66

GOOSE

GOAT

HARE

OX

BUTTERFLY

WOLF

ELEPHANT

TEDDY BEAR

DOG

DONKEY

PAPER BAG HATS

Here and on the next page are 5 hats you can make. The only materials needed are paper grocery bags and some cotton.
It will take only a few minutes to make each hat.

A CROWN

Cut across the bag 2 times, the first time to make the saw-toothed top of the crown, the second time to make the straight-bottom edge.

AN AVIATOR'S HELMET

First draw the goggles on the front of the bag. Beneath it draw the outline of the face. Cut along the dotted outline. This will make a hole through which the wearer's face can look out. Do not cut out the goggles, but do cut off the bottom of the bag to the right length, which is at the wearer's shoulders.

A SANTA CLAUS HAT

First cut off the top of the bag. Then tie to make the tassel. Then place the bag over the wearer's head and shorten the bag for the right length. Then paste some cotton at the bottom of Santa's hat.

AN OVERSEAS CAP

Cut across the bag in the manner shown here. The folded parts of the closed parts of the closed end of the bag will be like the folded gussets of an overseas cap.

A PILL BOX

Roll the open end of a bag twice to form the up-turned brim of the pill box. Then cut off as much of closed end of the bag as necessary to make the hat fit your head. Fold the cut end inward and fasten folds together with a two-pronged paper fastener.

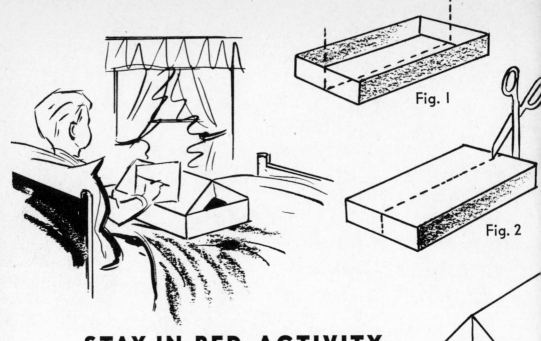

Fig. 1

Fig. 2

Fig. 4

STAY-IN-BED ACTIVITY BOX

Every child has days when he must stay in bed. For such days make for him a stay-in-bed activity box.

Obtain a large flat box such as the type used by stores to pack dresses in! Remove the cover. Find the center of the two narrow ends. Mark them and cut a slit at these marked places. Fig. 1.

Then using a ruler and a pencil draw a line across the back of the cover from one slit to the other. Then with scissors score the line lightly. Fig. 2. Do not cut through the cover. Now bend lightly along this line. Fig. 3.

Place the folded cover into the other part of the dress box. Brace it against the 2 long sides to make a slanting book-rest, or a writing stand. Fig. 4.

Keep pencils, crayons, and paper in the box, or even small toys. Such a stay-in-bed activity box will keep a child comfortably and happily occupied for a long time.

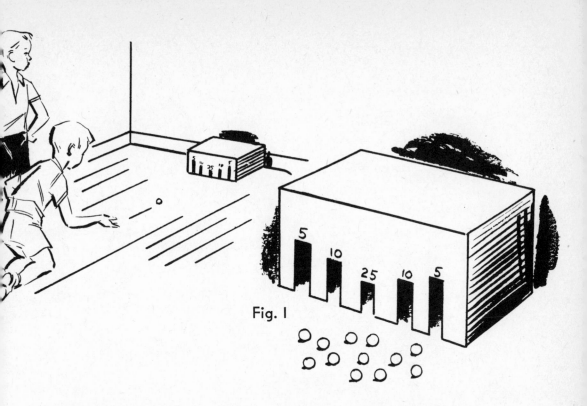

Fig. 1

A GAME PLAYED WITH MARBLES

This marble game often called "Stabling Your Horses" is easy to construct and great fun to play.

Use a cardboard shoe box for the table. Remove the cover. Turn the box upside down and cut 5 entrances to the stable, using one of the 2 long sides of the box for these entrances. The smallest entrance should be about 1 inch wide and $1\frac{1}{2}$ inches tall, and the longest about 2 inches wide and $2\frac{1}{2}$ inches tall. Mark over each entrance the figures 5, 10, and 25 as indicated in Fig. 1.

To play this game, place the shoe box stable against a wall. Then measure off a distance of 4 feet in front of it on the floor. Give each player 5 marbles depending upon the number of entrances. Each player rolls or shoots his marbles from the 4 foot marking, shooting all of them at each turn. The game may be continued as long as desired. However, it is well to reach a predetermined score, such as 100 or 250 before beginning the game. The player first obtaining this score wins the game.

CORK PRINTING

Cork stamps can be used to decorate bookmarks, wrapping paper, and boxes. Soak the cork in water before attempting to outline the design upon it. Find a design that will fit the end of the cork.

Ink the outline of the design on the cork. With a penknife cut away all parts of the surface so as to leave the design raised.

If the design you wish to use is too large to fit the end of a cork, split the cork in two, and use one of the flat surfaces of the halves.

Press the cut out design against a regular stamp pad, or one you have made from soaking 2 or 3 pieces of blotting paper in ink or dye in a small pan until it is well covered with ink or dye. Then stamp on a piece of cloth or paper.

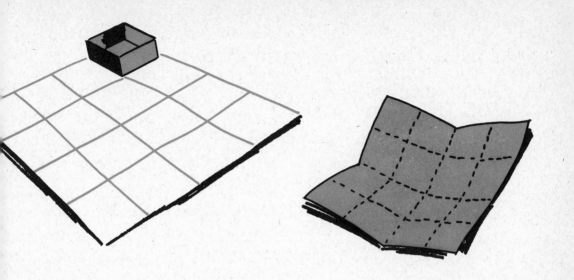

A FOLDED CHRISTMAS BOX

To make this box select a square of paper 4 times as long and 4 times as wide as you wish the finished box to be. Fold the paper through the center each way and open. Fold each edge to the center crease. Again fold each outer edge to the center. Open the paper and you will have a sheet divided into 64 squares. Draw along the folds exactly as indicated in the diagram. Cut on the heavy lines. Bend forward on folds A and B, and fasten tabs. Then bend forward on C and D and fasten. Make your first box of light weight paper. Use it as a pattern. Make the finished box of heavy white paper. Decorate it with cut-outs from Christmas cards or wrapping paper.

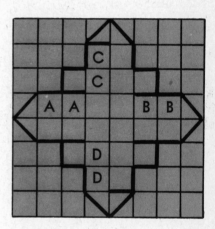

a Window Christmas Card

From a 6 by 10 inch piece of green construction paper make a folder measuring 5 inches by 6 inches. Fig. 1. Then from a piece of white paper cut a doorway measuring 3 inches by 4 inches. Fig. 2. Draw a window in the doorway. Cut around the window on three sides. Fig. 3.

Be sure to leave the fourth side attached to the door. Open the window. Lay the doorway on the upper side of the folder. Mark on the green paper the framework of the window. This will denote the place to paste a snapshot of yourself or a Christmas seal. Fig. 4. Remove the doorway. Paste picture or seal in place. Fig. 5. Then paste doorway in place. Be sure that the doorway is pasted so that the picture or seal will be looking out when the window is open. Do not put any paste on the window. Fig. 6.

On the inside page of the folder write a Christmas poem or message.

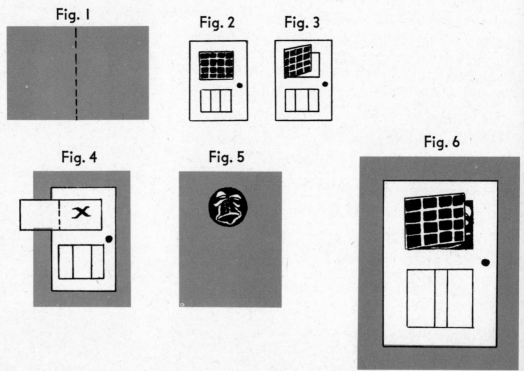

Fig. I Fig. 2 Fig. 3

Fig. 4 Fig. 5 Fig. 6

Christmas Tree

Fig. 3

Fig. 2

Trace and cut out pattern given in Fig. 1.

Place pattern on twice-folded piece of green construction paper. Trace around pattern. Be certain middle of tree is on the folded edge. Cut out. You will have a pair of trees.

Cut one tree at top, and one at the bottom. Fig. 2. Put trees together as shown in Fig. 3.

Make several of these trees. Paste gold stars and Santa Claus seals on them. Use to decorate dinner table and the mantelpiece.

Fig. 1

A SANTA CLAUS

Fig. 1

Attach pipe cleaners to base.

Fig. 2

Cut around the heavy black line.

Trace and cut out the Santa Claus pattern which appears on the next page. Use this pattern to make 2 tracings on heavy bright red cardboard. Match the copies. On the sides that face inward fasten 2 pipe cleaners with Scotch tape; as shown in Fig. 1. Glue 2 figures together. Paste cotton on Santa's suit and a tassel on his cap. Then fasten his feet to a cardboard base as shown in Fig. 2. Place cotton about the feet.

Use this Santa Claus for a table or window decoration.

STOCKINGS

Fig. I

Use the pattern given herewith to make Christmas stockings of felt. Fig. I. Decorate them with designs of stars, reindeer, trees, and Santas. These may be made with cloth, buttons, or sequins. Use a blanket stitch to put stocking parts together.

Pattern may be enlarged by using squared paper as shown.

Fig. 1

Fig. 2

yarn dolls

Fig. 3

Fig. 4

To make yarn dolls cut a piece of cardboard to measure 4 inches by 6 inches. Wind yarn around the cardboard 26 times beginning at the bottom of the cardboard. Fig. 1. Tie the yarn at the top and cut along the bottom. Fig. 2. Then tie again 1 inch from the top. This will form the head of the yarn doll.

Now separate 4 strands on each side for the arms. Tie the ends to make the arms. Fig. 3. Then measure down 3 inches from the top and tie as you did for the head. This will make the waist. Trim the ends to make the bottom of the skirt even. Fig. 4.

If you wish to make a boy doll instead of a girl doll, separate the yarn below the waist line into two parts. Tie the strands of each part together for feet. Fig. 5. Sew eyes, ears, and mouth with black or white yarn.

Fig. 5

Fig. 1

Fig. 2

BOOKMARKS

Fig. 3

Fig. 4

One of the easiest ways to make a bookmark is to cut off an envelope corner as shown in Fig. 1. Use a picture seal to decorate it. Fig. 2. You may use a cut out picture from a magazine instead of the seal. In that case you will need paste to seal the picture in place on the bookmark.

Another easy way in which to make a bookmark is to cut a strip of paper measuring 2 or 3 inches in width and 10 or 11 inches in length. Crease in the center. Fig. 3. On the upper side decorate with a picture. Then slide it over the page last read.

Sometimes it is possible to use a picture from a book's jacket to make an attractive bookmark for that particular book. Print the title of the book on the bookmark. Fig. 4.

In this way every book can have its special bookmark.

Little children like to look at pictures of familiar objects. It is easy to make a book of heavy cardboard that will give a very young picture-looker much enjoyment.

Cut 7 pieces of heavy cardboard, each to measure 7 inches by 10 inches. Then find large pictures of a dog, a cat, a rabbit, a cow, a horse, a sheep, and a pig. Paste each on one of the pieces of cardboard. Write or print in large letters the name of each animal underneath its picture.

Line the back of each picture with paper, cut to right size, and of the same color. Use adhesive tape to join the pages together. If desired, such tape can be used to reenforce the edges of each page. A coating of clear shellac will make the pages more durable.

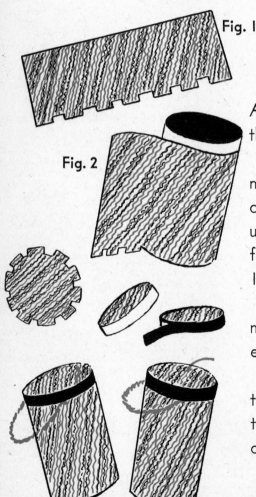

Fig. 1

Fig. 2

A YARN

A yarn holder is easy to make if you follow these simple directions and sketches.

Select an oatmeal box. With a pencil mark a ring around the box just below the cover. Remove cover. Cut a strip of figured paper $\frac{1}{2}$ inch longer than distance from marked ring to bottom of box and 1 inch wider than its circumference. Fig. 1.

Notch bottom edge. Fig. 2. Paste strip neatly to outside of box, pasting notched edge to the bottom.

Line box with paper that harmonizes with the outside covering. Then cut 2 circles of the lining paper to fit the inside and outside of the bottom of the box. Paste in place.

ACCORDION PICTURE BOOK

HOLDER

Cover the lid with a circle of figured paper, notched in the same manner as the outside cover. Paste in place. Cover rim with a strip of paper the exact width of the rim and 1/2 inch longer than its circumference. Paste in place. Make 2 small holes in the top of the box through which to fasten a pretty cord for a handle.

Punch a hole in the center of the cover, just big enough for a piece of yarn to slip through it easily. Place a ball of yarn in the box, pass the end through the hole in the cover. Place cover on box. The yarn holder is ready to be presented to a knitter.

A welcome Christmas gift for a small boy or girl

A Peter Rabbit Toy

Use the outline drawing given on the next page. Cut out and trace 3 times on a piece of wood. Fig. 1. This will make two pieces for the side and one for the middle. This done, glue the 3 pieces together in sandwich-style. Fig. 2. Put in a clamp. Keep there until glue is dry. Remove, trim uneven edges and sandpaper.

Use a thin piece of wood for a stand or carriage. Attach rabbit to this piece. Add 2 side pieces to match. Nail in place. Fig. 3.

Cut 4⅜ inch thick pieces from a broomstick. Attach to carriage. Add a metal washer between wheels and carriage in order to let wheels turn easily. Fig. 4.

Attach a string to the carriage. Fig. 5.

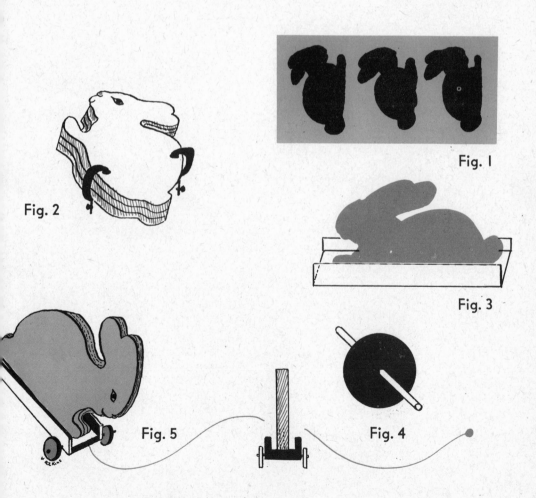

Fig. 1

Fig. 2

Fig. 3

Fig. 5

Fig. 4

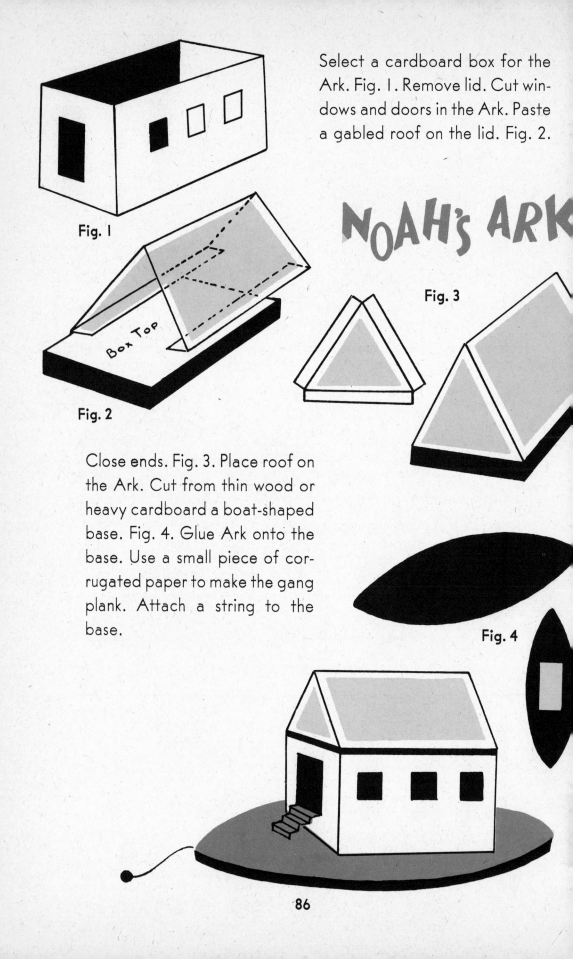

Select a cardboard box for the Ark. Fig. 1. Remove lid. Cut windows and doors in the Ark. Paste a gabled roof on the lid. Fig. 2.

Fig. 1

NOAH'S ARK

Fig. 2

Box Top

Fig. 3

Close ends. Fig. 3. Place roof on the Ark. Cut from thin wood or heavy cardboard a boat-shaped base. Fig. 4. Glue Ark onto the base. Use a small piece of corrugated paper to make the gang plank. Attach a string to the base.

Fig. 4

EANUT ANIMALS FOR THE ARK

With some pieces of stiff paper, milk bottle tops, toothpicks, and pipe cleaners you can make peanuts look like an elephant, a camel, a kangaroo, a giraffe, or a monkey.

Fig. 1

To make the camel, select a peanut with a large hump. Cut the head and neck as shown in Fig. 1. Ink in eyes and mouth. Slide head into a slit made in the peanut. Attach a piece of darning cotton for a tail. Use 3 straight toothpicks or 3 pieces of pipe cleaners for the hind legs and 1 front leg. Bend another toothpick or pipe cleaner to make the fourth leg. Attached to the peanut, this leg will make the camel appear to be walking.

Select a peanut the shape of which most closely resembles the body and head of an elephant. Cut 2 cardboard front legs, then 2 cardboard hind legs. Fig. 2. Then 2 paper ears Fig. 3, and a paper trunk. Fig. 4. Paste ears, trunk and a yarn tail, in their proper positions. Slide legs into slits made in sides of the peanut. Use 2 toothpicks to make the tusks.

Now begin making your own patterns for other peanut animals as pictured here.

Fig. 3

Fig. 2

Fig. 4

87

Fig. 1

Get two orange crate ends. Nail the flat sides together. Fig. 1. Use door stops for legs. Screw them firmly into place to form a four-legged footstool. Fig. 2. Pad the top with cotton or excelsior and cover with a piece of cloth that has been cut to meet the requirements of the padded top. Fig. 3. Cover the underside with some kind of material. Fig. 4. Then cover the padded top with cretonne, denim or striped pillow-ticking. Fig. 5. Finish with a pleated ruffle of the same material and braid. You may use fringe instead of the pleated ruffle.

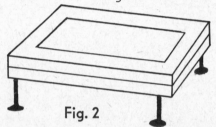

Fig. 2

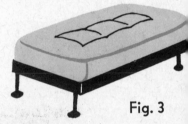

Fig. 3

A PRETTY FOOTSTOOL FOR MOTHER

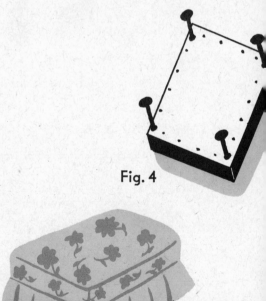

Fig. 4

Fig. 5

A CRAYON TAPESTRY

Select a design. Map out color areas on it. Trace the design on cloth, using a sharp pencil to do this. Fill in this design with well-sharpened crayons, using vertical and horizontal strokes until the desired color tones have been acquired.

After the coloring is done place material between layers of damp cloth or papers and press with a warm iron.

Finish the tapestry with any needlework that will give a finished appearance to your design. Mount on a rod for hanging.

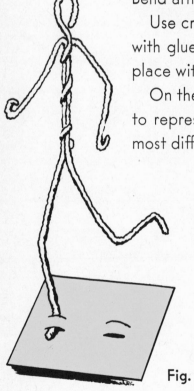

Fig. 1

PIPE CLEANER DOLLS

Bend 3 pipe cleaners as shown in Fig. 1. Twist lower ends of headpiece around the middle sections of arms and legs to form the body. Fig. 2.

Cover the head loop with cotton and a piece of white cloth. Gather in the back and sew firmly. Paint in facial features. Use yarn or curled strips of paper for hair. Sew or glue in place.

To make the figure stand use a cardboard base 2 inches square. Cut 2 slits 1/8 inch apart in it. Slip one foot through these slits. Fig. 2. If doll is top heavy cut a second slit in base and anchor the other foot of the doll. Bend arms at elbows and legs at knees for action poses.

Use crepe paper or cloth to dress dolls. Put together with glue or needle and thread or simply hold parts in place with fingers and tie with thread.

On the opposite page are pipe cleaner dolls dressed to represent Hansel and Gretel, and patterns for the most difficult parts of their costumes to make.

Fig. 2

Paper Curls

HANSEL and GRETEL

Overlap and paste opposite edge here

Paste to waist

Fold

Gretel's cap
Overlap A and B, paste

Turn up points of cap

A   B

91

a *Whirly-twirly*
MERRY-GO-ROUND

This MERRY-GO-ROUND will whirl round and round at a touch
of your finger or when the wind blows against the flaps under
its roof top. You will have fun making it and watching the
figures fly through the air.

First, collect these materials: a square piece of lightweight
cardboard, 8 x 8 inches; 2 pieces of heavy cardboard, 8 x 8
inches; a four-inch piece of ½ inch dowel; glue; a thumbtack;
transparent tape; tempera; figures you may draw or cut from
magazines.

Then follow the directions and pictures shown on the next
page. When you have finished the construction, paint the base
and roof with your brightest colors. Cut paper flags and
streamers to add to the gaiety. Pin or tape them in place.

Now set the merry-go-round spinning round and round!

. 1. Draw an **X** from corners to find center. Draw #1 outside circle.

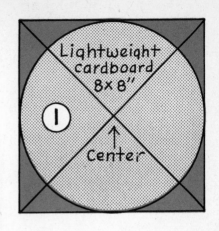

2. Draw a circle 1 inch inside #1. Draw center circle.

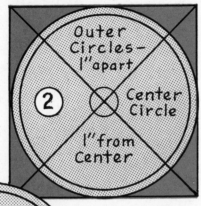

3. Mark flaps and cut on heavy lines. Fold down on dotted lines.

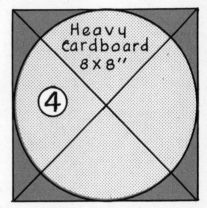

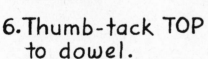

BASE. 4. Cut two circles. Glue them together.

5. Glue dowel to BASE.

6. Thumb-tack TOP to dowel.

7. Tape figures to TOP-edge. Add flags and streamers for decoration.

OLD MOTHER HUBBARD AND HER DOG

Make a tracing of the pattern for Mother Hubbard. Place it on the fold of a sheet of paper. Trace around it. Cut out. Spread the pattern flat and crayon or ink in Mother Hubbard's facial features. Paste back together. Bend feet to stand on a flat surface. Place Mother Hubbard and her dog beside the cupboard.

To make the dog and cupboard, follow the directions given with the sketches on the next page.

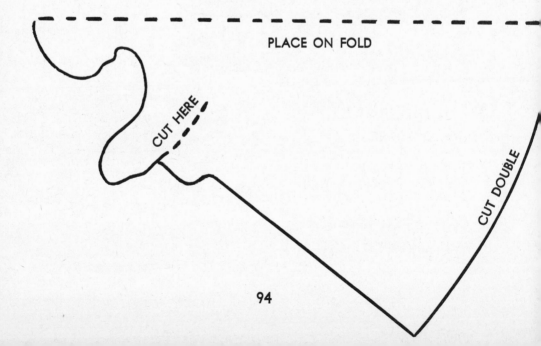

PLACE ON FOLD

CUT HERE

CUT DOUBLE

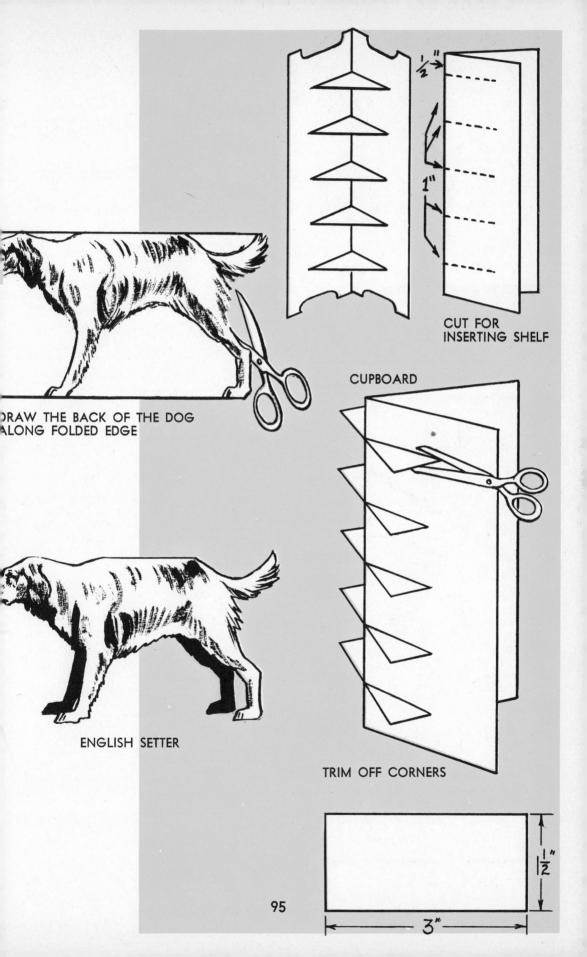

CUT FOR
INSERTING SHELF

DRAW THE BACK OF THE DOG
ALONG FOLDED EDGE

CUPBOARD

ENGLISH SETTER

TRIM OFF CORNERS

95

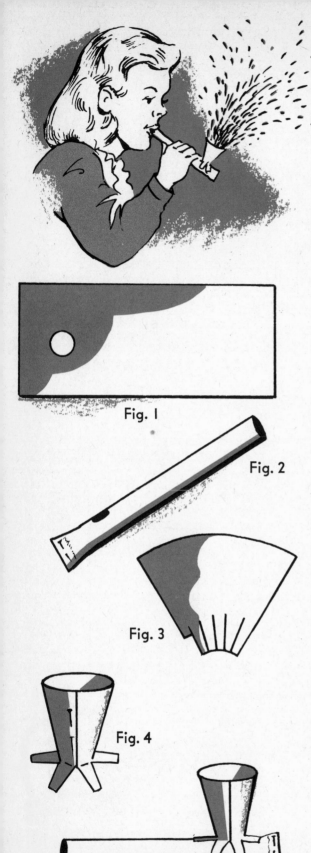

Fig. I

Fig. 2

Fig. 3

Fig. 4

Fig. 5

A Sparkling Paper Pipe

A sparkling paper pipe will furnish great fun on the Fourth of July.

Take a strip of stiff paper $3\frac{1}{2}$ inches wide and 11 inches long. Cut a hole in one end. Fig. I. Paste the 2 lengthwise edges together to form a hollow tube. Pin up the open end nearest to the hole. Fig. 2. Cut the bowl of pipe in the form of Fig. 3, making it about 4 inches across the widest part; slash the lower edge and paste the pipe-bowl into a funnel shape by bringing the 2 sides together. Fig. 4.

Fasten the bowl over the hole in the pipestem. Glue in place. Fig. 5.

Make a supply of gold, silver, red, blue, yellow, and green paper cut very small. Fill the pipe bowl half-full, with bits of the colored paper. The brighter the colors, the more sparkling the fireworks.

Place the open end of the pipe stem to your lips and blow.

a clothespin basket

Fig. 1

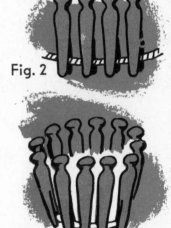

Fig. 2

Fig. 3

Obtain a piece of wire to form a circle that is large enough to hold 24 clothespins and to provide for an overlapping of the ends to close the circle. Wrap the wire circle with narrow strips of crepe paper until it is thick enough to fit snugly into the clothespins. Fig. 1. Slip the pins around the circle. Fig. 2. To hold them in place around the wire, weave strips of crepe paper, or ribbon in and out among the heads of the clothespins. Fig. 3. Fasten securely. Then wrap a second piece of wire with crepe paper or ribbon until it is about the thickness of a lead pencil. Bend the wound wire to form a handle for the basket. Fasten the handle securely to the lower ring of wire and to the heads of 2 clothespins. Fig. 4. Crepe-paper-wrapped-spool-wire makes a good handle fastener. Paint the basket white or brown or blue. Dry thoroughly. Place a glass or small flower pot inside the basket.

Fig. 4

Rocking Horse

On the next page is a pattern for a small rocking horse.

Make a copy of it. Then trace your pattern on a sheet of lightweight cardboard. Cut out.

Fold the cut-out double horse in half so that the 2 sides match. Fasten the 2 sides of the horse's back together with a paper clip. Bend the base up between the rounded ends of the rockers.

Give the small rocking horse a gentle push. It will start rocking back and forth.

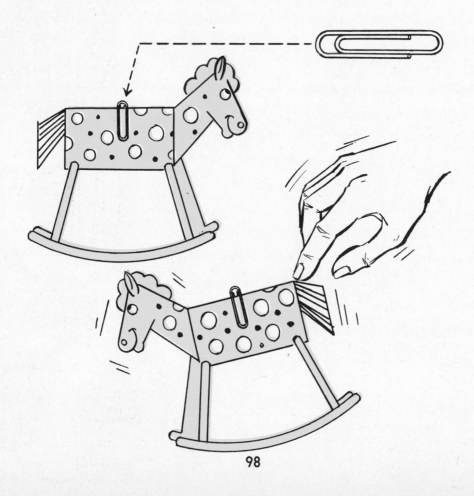

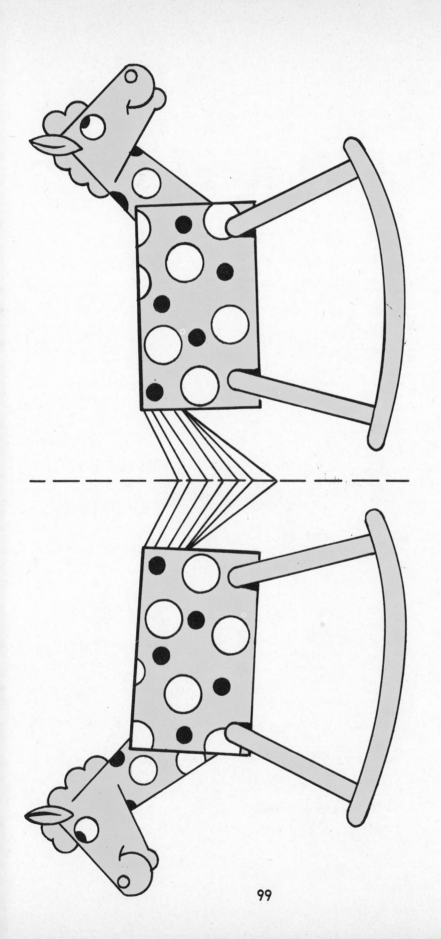

CLOTH APPLIQUE

Pictures made from cloth can be used to decorate gift boxes, luncheon sets, book covers, knitting boxes, and sewing bags.

The design shown here was used to decorate a covering for a sewing scrapbook. Try making one. It's fun. It is great fun, too, to create cloth pictures using bits of lace and ribbon as shown on the next page.

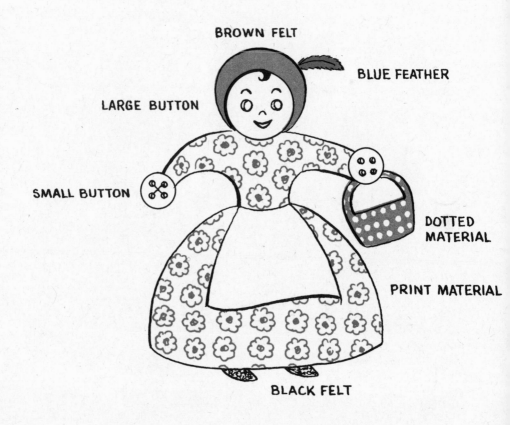

PEANUT PUPPET

Select 5 peanuts of about the same size to make the body, legs and arms of the puppet, and a smaller peanut to make the head.

With a darning needle carefully run a strong black thread through the top of the head. With black ink draw the eyes, nose, and mouth. Paste on 2 white paper ears to the head. Fig. 1.

From white paper make the hat, using Figs. 2 & 3 as patterns. Slip finished hat onto the peanut head. Run thread through it.

Attach legs and arms to the body with strong black thread.

Fasten a strong thread to the end of each arm. Tie the ends of these strings and that of the one attached to the head to a 1/4 inch dowel. Notch to prevent thread from slipping. Fig. 4.

Use the dowel to make the puppet perform.

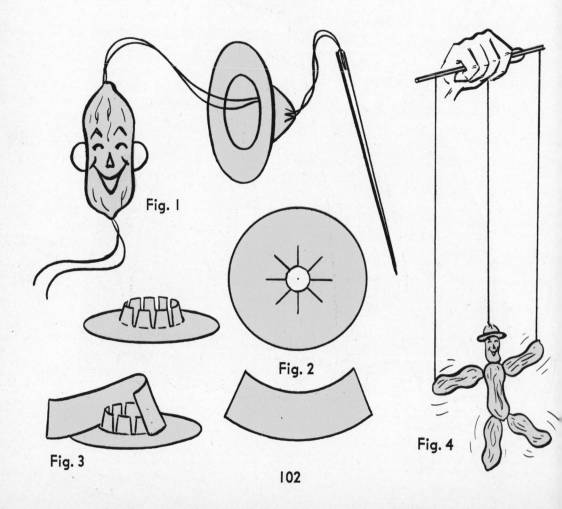

Fig. 1

Fig. 2

Fig. 3

Fig. 4

A DANCING CLOWN FINGER PUPPET

Trace the clown picture on this page. Color his suit yellow with large black dots.

Cut off the legs and paste the legless picture on a piece of cardboard, the kind the laundryman puts in men's shirts is a good type to use. Now cut around the clown, cutting through the cardboard. Then using a penny make the outline of two round holes in the bottom of the figure. Cut these out. Place your fingers through the holes. Make them move so that the clown will walk, jump, stumble, take a nose dive, or dance.

Make several of these puppets. When your friends come to visit, ask them to join you in a show of clown tricks.

CRAYON BATIK

Hundreds of years ago the Javenese learned that wax repels water. Knowing this, they created a design upon cloth, covered it with melted wax, dipped the cloth in dye, and then removed the wax. The result was a design against a background of the dyed cloth. The process and the cloth made in this way are known as batik.

To make a crayon batik draw a design upon a piece of cloth. Select a design that is composed of solid areas to be filled with the crayons. A bowl of gay-colored flowers makes an excellent design. Fill in design with crayons. Use them heavily.

Cover the entire picture with black water color paint. Use plenty of paint on the brush. Put aside to dry. When completely dry your pictures will have a solid background out of which will shine many beautiful colors.

The WOODLAND SPECIAL

To make the cars for this special train cut 1 inch wood into blocks that measure 6 inches in width and 9 inches in length. Each block of wood makes a car. Fasten a screw eye in the center front of each car and a screw hook in the rear of each car. These hooks and eyes are "the couplings" that will hold the cars of "The Woodland Special" together. Fig. 1.

To make the wheels saw 1 inch lengths from the roller of a discarded window shade. Fig. 2. Each car, of course, will need 4 of these wheels. Drill a hole through the center of each wheel for the nail axles. If the nail is driven directly through the wheel it has a tendency to split it. The wheels can be made to move easily if a washer is placed between them and the "car body." Fig. 3.

Tie a strong cord or small rope to the screw eye of the front car.

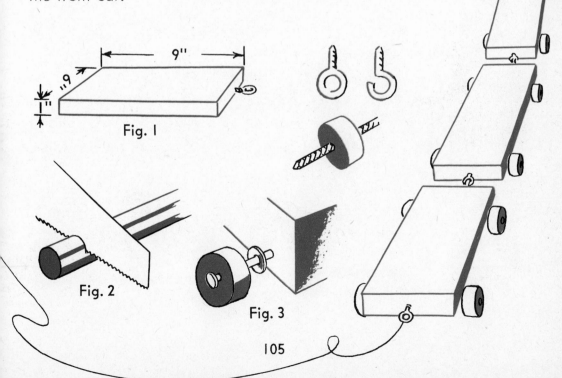

Fig. 1

Fig. 2

Fig. 3

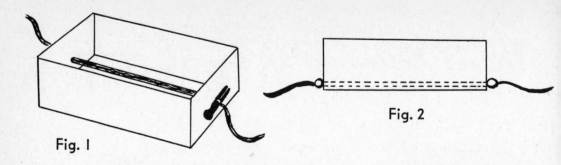

Fig. 1

Fig. 2

shoe box train

Remove the covers from 3 or 4 shoe boxes. Punch a hole near the bottom of each of the box ends. Obtain a length of cord that is long enough to pass through the insides of the boxes and to provide a length for pulling the train. Then tie a clothespin on one end of the cord. Beginning on the outside of one box, run the cord through the hole so that it comes through into the inside of the box. The clothespin will prevent the cord from slipping out of the end of the box. Pull the cord along the bottom of the box and out the other end of the box. Fig. 1. Knot a second clothespin on the outside of this end of the box. Fig. 2. Then run the cord through the other boxes in the same way. Fig. 3. Be sure to knot a clothespin at the other end of the rope. This will make a handle.

The shoe box train is now ready to be loaded with toys and pulled across the room by a toddler.

Fig. 3

the box limited

Use box-tops for the bases of all the cars for this train, and milk bottle tops or button moulds for their wheels. Attach the wheels to the bases with two-pronged paper fasteners. Fasten loosely enough to allow the wheels to turn easily.

To make the tops of the cars use smaller boxes than those used to make the bases.

Use an oatmeal box for the top part of the engine. Glue in place. Cut little slits in the box for the stacks and bell. Make the bell and stacks from black construction paper.

Decorate each car according to its use.

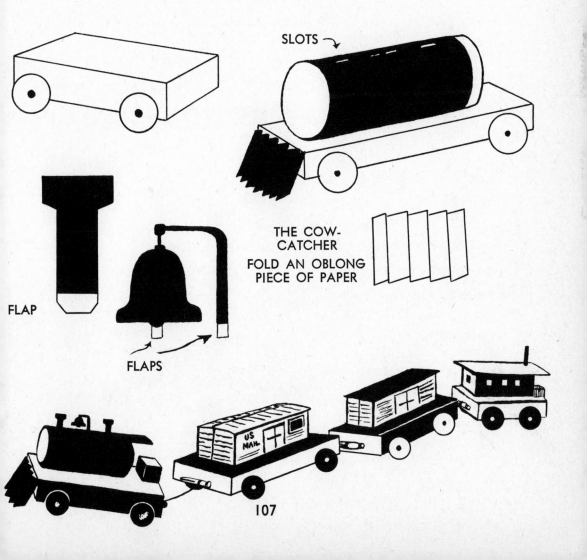

SLOTS

FLAP

FLAPS

THE COW-
CATCHER

FOLD AN OBLONG
PIECE OF PAPER

US
MAIL

Fig. 1

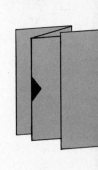
Fig. 2

AN ENGINEER'S CAP

To make an engineer's cap cut a strip of blue construction paper to measure $2\frac{1}{2}$ inches wide and 20 inches long. Make cuts $\frac{1}{2}$ inch deep to form tabs on one side of this strip of paper. Fig. 1. Then cut a circle $6\frac{1}{2}$ inches in diameter to make the top of the cap. Paste the ends of the 20 inch strip together, bend its tabs toward the center. Paste them to the top of the cap. Fig. 2. Cut out a visor. Cut slits into it to make tabs. Fig. 3. Paste the visor tabs inside the cap band. Fig. 4.

To finish the cap cut a small circle of $1\frac{3}{4}$ inches in diameter from white paper. Write the initials of your railroad on it. Paste in place. Fig. 5.

A WHISTLE FOR YOUR TRAIN

Obtain a piece of paper. Fold it into 4 parts. Fig. 1. Cut a hole in center fold. Fig. 2. Then hold the front fold against your lips and blow into it. You will be delighted with the first class whistle you have made for your train.

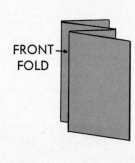
Fig. 1

FRONT→
FOLD

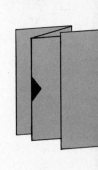
Fig. 2

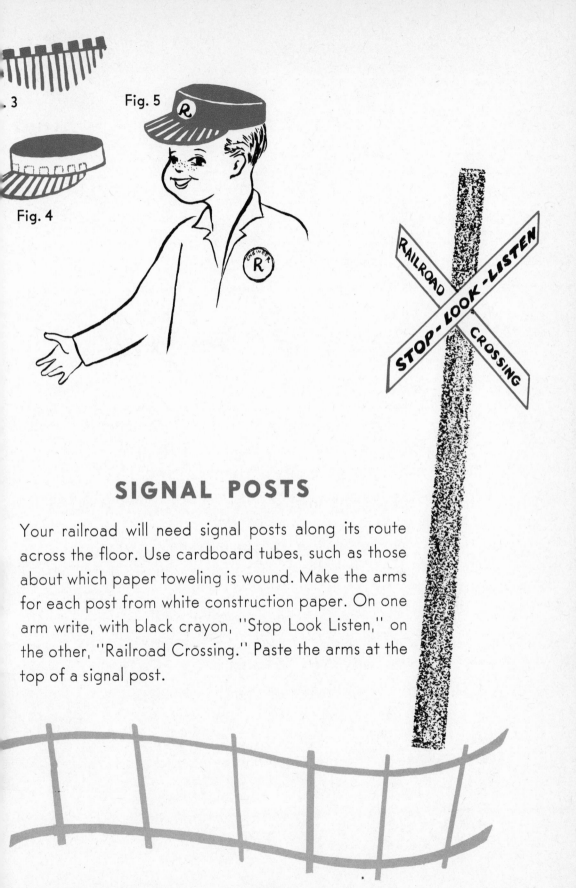

Fig. 3

Fig. 5

Fig. 4

SIGNAL POSTS

Your railroad will need signal posts along its route across the floor. Use cardboard tubes, such as those about which paper toweling is wound. Make the arms for each post from white construction paper. On one arm write, with black crayon, "Stop Look Listen," on the other, "Railroad Crossing." Paste the arms at the top of a signal post.

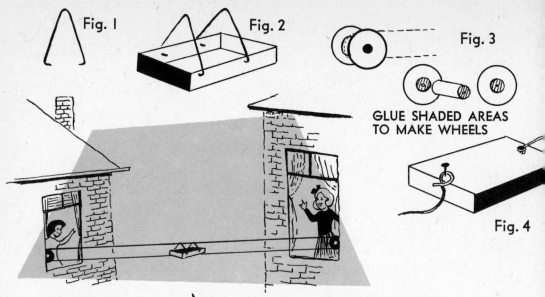

Fig. 1

Fig. 2

Fig. 3

GLUE SHADED AREAS
TO MAKE WHEELS

Fig. 4

AN AERIAL RAILROAD

The day a snowstorm keeps you indoors is just the day to make an aerial railroad. After the storm has spent its fury you can erect the railroad in the place where you can enjoy it the most.

All that is needed to make the car for this aerial railroad is a cigar box and 2 pieces of wire. Bend the 2 wires to form the shape shown in Fig. 1. Insert the lower bent-in-ends of these wire forms into holes drilled through the sides of the cigar box. Fig. 2.

The aerial railroad consists of a long piece of strong cord which passes over grooved wheels at the end of the railroad. Metal grooved wheels can be obtained at a hardware store but it's fun to make them from pieces of wood. Fig. 3.

When ready to erect the railroad out-of-doors, mount the car as shown in the sketch at the top of this page. Tie the 2 ends of the cord to small nails driven in the ends of the car. Fig. 4. Pull the cord as tight as possible when it is being tied to the box. A taut rope will prevent its sagging under the weight of the car when it is carrying a heavy load.

It's great fun to send loads over this railroad from your home to that of your friend who lives next door.

A WINDLASS

To make a windlass that will carry a pail or a basket from the ground to a third story window obtain a square piece of wood. Remove a section from one side as shown in Fig. 1.

Add 2 upright pieces of wood to this base. Nail through the bottom. Fig. 2.

Before nailing in place, put them together and bore a hole through each at the proper height to hold the axle. A dowel stick makes an excellent axle. Fig. 3.

Now mount a large-sized spool on the axle and fit the axle into the holes cut for it in the upright sections. Fig. 4.

To one end of the axle attach a handle in the manner shown in Fig. 4.

Tie a length of strong string around the spool, fasten a pail or basket at the other end.

Then begin winding the string. Up will come the basket or pail.

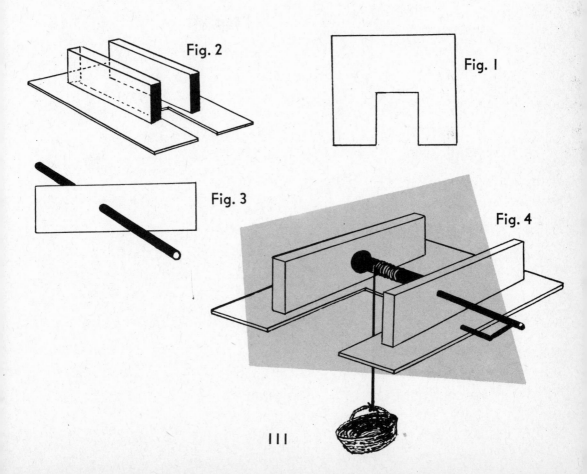

Fig. 2

Fig. 1

Fig. 3

Fig. 4

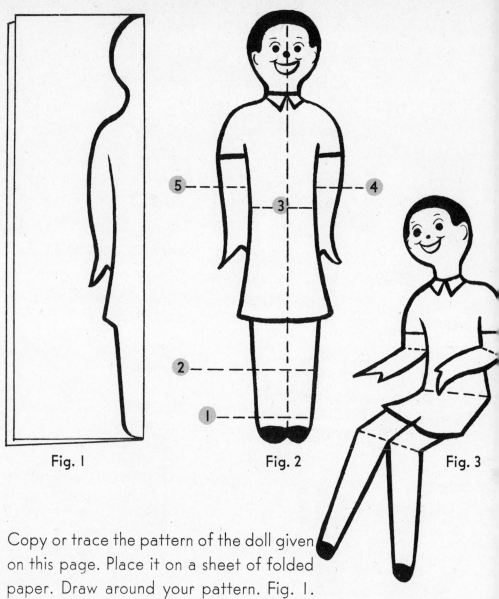

Fig. 1   Fig. 2   Fig. 3

Copy or trace the pattern of the doll given
on this page. Place it on a sheet of folded
paper. Draw around your pattern. Fig. 1.
Cut out. Unfold. Then draw in the facial features and clothes. Fig.
2. Now cut along the center fold up to the second dotted line.
Then make 2 cuts up to the dotted lines marked 4 and 5.

Now fold up to dotted lines marked 1. Fold to make the doll's
feet. Fold legs back at dotted lines marked 2. Then fold the doll
forward at the waist, dotted line 3. Now fold the arms at elbows,
dotted lines 4 and 5. Fig. 2.

On the next page are patterns for two other paper dolls. Study
sketches carefully before doing any cutting and folding.

PAPER
DOLLS

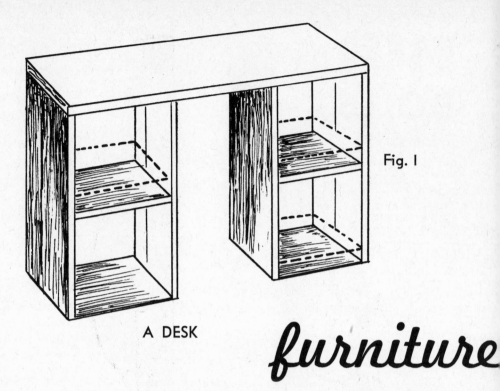

A DESK

Fig. I

furniture

A BOOKCASE

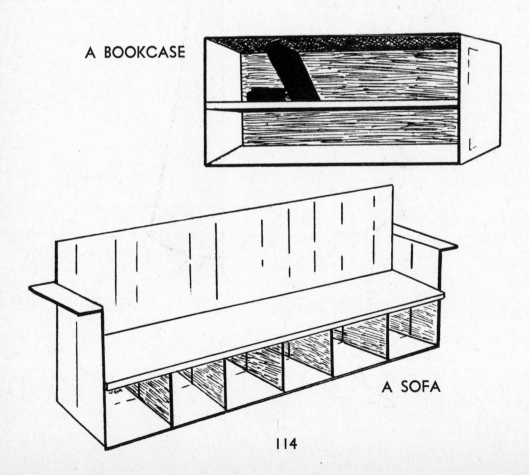

A SOFA

Start your furniture making with 2 orange crates. Stand them on end 1½ feet apart. Place a board that reaches over them and across the space between. Nail in place. To add shelves mark space within the crates at the levels you desire other shelves to be placed. Fig. 1. At these markings nail in small supports made of narrow strips of wood. Fig. 1. Rest the shelves on these supports.

Once you have started making furniture from boxes it will be fun to arrange them in different positions to make tables, chairs, bookcases, and settees, and easy too, if you study the sketches given here.

from boxes

PAD AND COVER

A DRESSING TABLE

A CHAIR

A FIVE-

The stars in the blue field of the American flag are five-pointed. It was Betsy Ross who convinced General Washington that it was a simple matter to cut a five-pointed star from a folded sheet of paper or cloth. And, you, too, will find it as easy to cut a five-pointed star if you will make a careful study of these sketches and follow exactly the directions given herewith—

First fold a square of paper through the middle as shown in Fig. 1.

With the fold at the top bring the right hand corner over to a point on the left-hand side of the sheet of paper which is about 2/3 of the way down from the left hand corner. Fig. 2.

Then fold the upper right side over once more as indicated by the dotted line in Fig. 2.

Now fold the left-hand corner of the fold over to the right edge. Fig. 3.

Cut across the folds at an angle, such as the one indicated in Fig. 4. If you desire longer and sharper points, cut at a sharper angle.

Your unfolded star should look like the one depicted in Fig. 5.

Five-pointed stars can be used to make flags, to decorate Christmas trees, packages, boxes, cards, toy crowns, and play costumes.

You might put these on a Christmas tree!

or hang them in your window

POINTED STAR

Fig. 1

Fig. 2

Fig. 3

Fig. 4

You could be Cinderella's Fairy Godmother!

He's the King in your neighborhood play!

Fig. 5

STAND-UP
ANIMALS

The stand-up animals found here and on the following pages may be cut from oak tag or lightweight cardboard. Trace the patterns given on these pages. Cut according to direc-

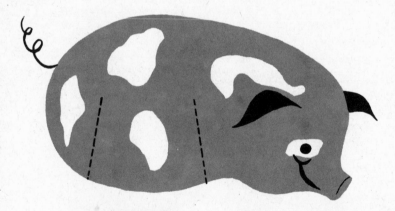

CUT ON DOTTED LINE

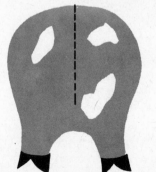

MAKE TWO OF THIS PATTERN

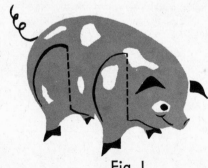

Fig. I

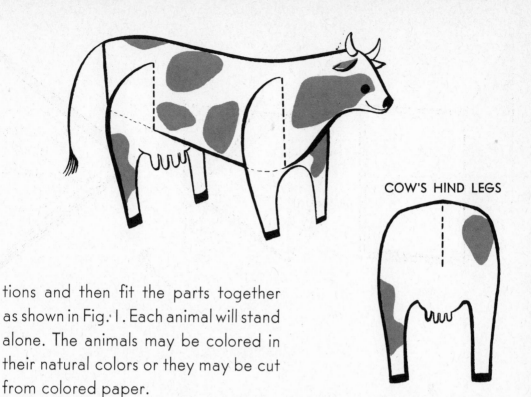

COW'S HIND LEGS

tions and then fit the parts together
as shown in Fig. I. Each animal will stand
alone. The animals may be colored in
their natural colors or they may be cut
from colored paper.

COW'S FRONT LEGS

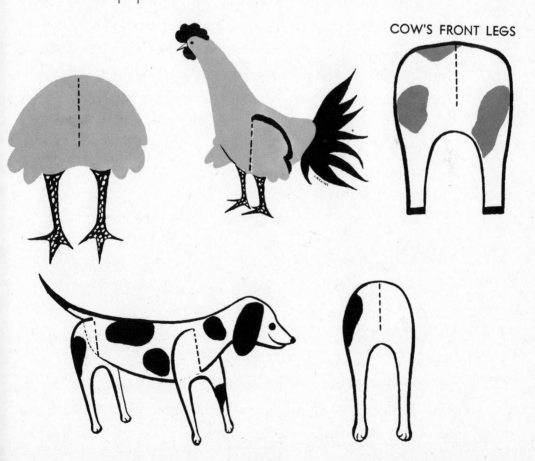

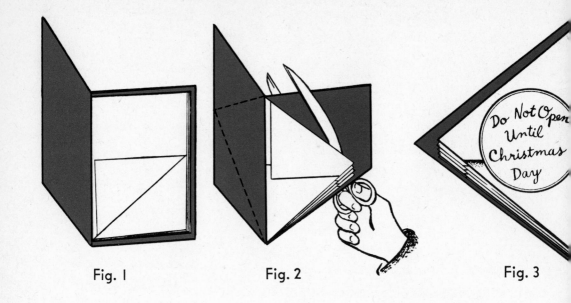

Fig. 1   Fig. 2   Fig. 3

A BOOK OF SECRETS

You can have fun and more fun with a book of secrets. First of all obtain a five-cent notebook. Lay it on a table before you. Lift up the lower edge of the first page and fold it up along the place where the notebook is stitched together. Fig. 1. Do the same with the upper edge of the page. This double folding brings the page to a point. Repeat the folding process with each page in the notebook. When the folding has been completed, cut down the covers of the notebook with a pair of sharp scissors. This will change your rectangular notebook into one of a triangular shape. Fig. 2.

You are now ready to ask your friends to write in your book of secrets. To do this each one unfolds a page, writes a message inside, refolds the page, seals it with a pretty seal, and then writes the date on which the sealed message is to be read. Fig. 3.

A book of secrets makes an excellent birthday or Christmas gift. For such a gift make the covers attractive with decorative paper or cloth.

Fig. 1

Fig. 2

VALENTINE HEARTS

It is easy to make valentine hearts. Fold a piece of paper. Draw upon this fold half of a heart. Fig. 1. Cut out on the curved line. Open. Use this heart for a pattern. Place it upon a sheet of red paper. Trace around the outline of the heart. Cut on this outline. Fig. 2.

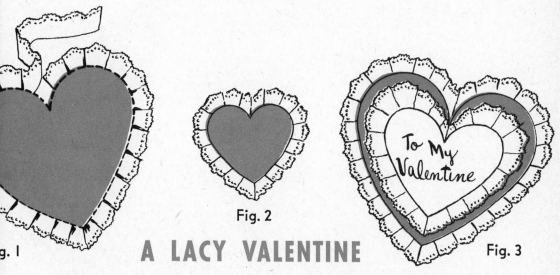

Fig. 2

Fig. 1

A LACY VALENTINE

Fig. 3

Paste a ruffle of lace around the edge of a red cardboard heart. Fig. 1. Paste over this heart a red heart as shown in Fig. 2.

Edge a tiny white heart with lace as you did the first red one. Paste it upon the red one. Fig. 3. Write on this heart "To My Valentine."

STENCILING LEAVES

A delightful way of keeping a leaf record is to make stencils of them. These stencils can be used to decorate doll house wallpaper, book covers, and an unbleached muslin tablecloth.

A stencil is a pattern which is cut in heavy paper or thin metal. This pattern-design is made with connected openings. To make, obtain a piece of cardboard. Place a leaf upon it. Draw around it. Then draw a second line close to the first one. Next cut out the outline space between the two lines leaving connecting parts. Place the stencil on a piece of paper or cloth. Use thumbtacks or pins to hold in place. Outline the openings. Remove the stencil. Fill in the shapes with crayons.

When stenciling unbleached muslin, use a brush to apply paint to the surfaces seen through the openings in the stencil. Fix the color by laying a damp cloth over the stencil and pressing with a warm iron.

Tied-Dye

Dyeing cloth to obtain pretty patterns is an old art. Such cloth may be used to make table covers, book covers, scarfs, or·curtains.

To make a piece of tied-dye cloth just follow these directions—

Select a favorite color; then prepare the dye according to the directions on the package. Use a square piece of an old sheet for your first experiment. Plan the design. Gather the fold at the desired points. Fig. 1. Wrap string tightly about the folds. Fig. 2. Tie the string in a bow so that it may be removed easily after the dyeing. Immerse the tied cloth in the dye. Rinse. Untie. Dry. Press. Fig. 3 shows the material after it has been dyed and pressed.

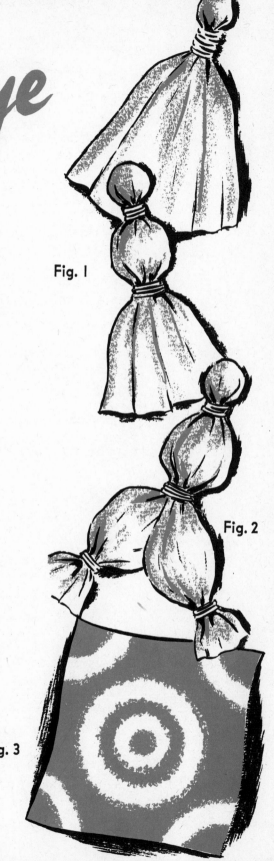

Fig. 1

Fig. 2

Fig. 3

A FLOWER BASKET VALENTINE

Obtain a round paper lace doily. Fold once. Fig. 1. Find the center of the fold. Then fold the right edges inward toward the center. Crease in place. Fig. 2. Do the same with the left edges. When this has been done, you will have a figure similar to Fig. 3. Paste a small red heart on each side of the basket. Attach a pipe cleaner handle in the manner indicated in Fig. 4. Cut 10 or 12 pipe cleaners, each into 2 parts of various lengths. Attach, with Scotch tape, tiny red hearts to the pipe cleaner stems. Fill the basket with these flowers. Tie a small bow of ribbon to the top of the handle. Glue onto each end of the ribbon a tiny heart. On one write "To My," on the other "Valentine."

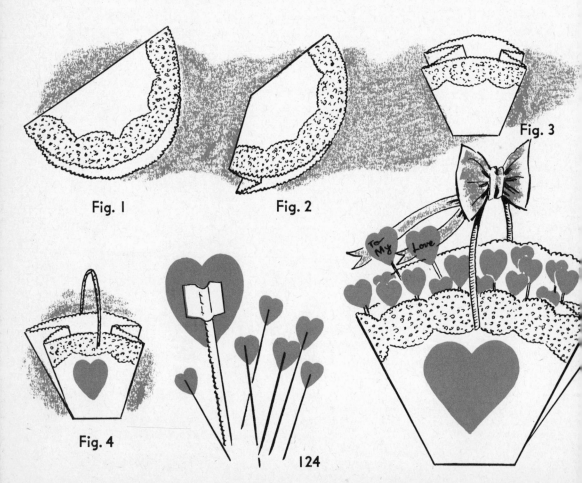

Fig. 1

Fig. 2

Fig. 3

Fig. 4

124

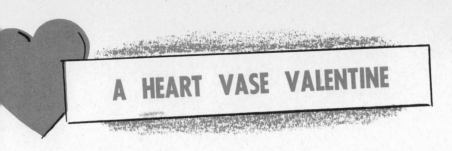

A HEART VASE VALENTINE

Cut from a piece of corrugated paper a large heart. Cut from red construction paper 2 hearts slightly larger than the corrugated one. Use them to cover the corrugated heart. Fig. 1. Now cut small and medium-sized hearts from red paper. Mount them on pipe cleaner stems. Use Scotch tape to do this. Push the heart flowers into the corrugated heart. Fig. 2. Vary the lengths to make an attractive bouquet. Paper flowers may be used with the heart ones.

Mount the heart vase on another piece of corrugated paper which has been covered with red or white construction paper. Cut a slit in this paper stand. Stick the vase into the slot. Reinforce from the back with Scotch tape.

Before mounting the vase into place write in white ink an appropriate valentine greeting on it.

Fig. 1

To My Valentine

Fig. 2

BUTTON PICTURES

Button pictures are made by pasting, tying, or sewing buttons onto a piece of heavy paper and adding a few ink lines and bits of colored paper to complete the pictures.

Study the sketches given here. Notice how the big buttons are used to make the bodies of the man, the bird, and the cat, and smaller ones for the head, and still smaller ones to make the man's neck, arms, and legs.

You may use colored buttons, such as blue ones for the bird, and black ones for the cat. It's very easy to cut from paper the bird's beak and tail and add its legs and claws with pen and ink, and just as easy to fashion the cat's ears and tail and to ink in the cat's whiskers.

You may use these button figures to decorate Valentine, Halloween, and birthday cards.

TIED-DYE BOOKCOVER

Attractive book covers can be made from tied-and-dyed cloth.
See page 123 for directions.

To make these book covers follow carefully directions given
with the pattern shown on this page. Be sure to put the name
of the book on its new cover.

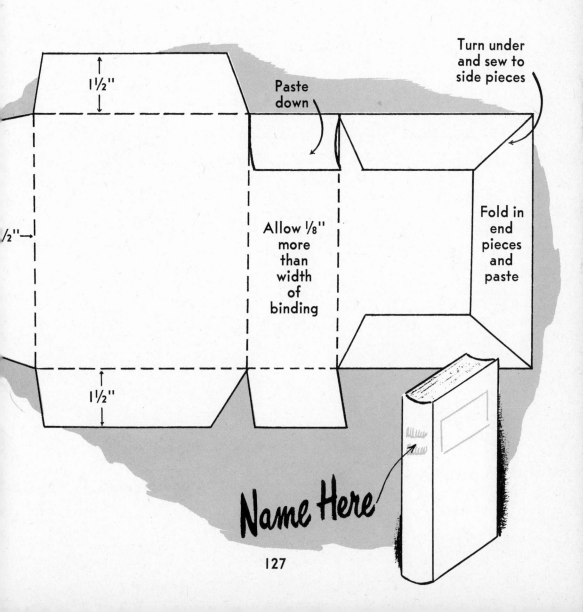

1½"

Paste
down

Turn under
and sew to
side pieces

½"→

Allow ⅛"
more
than
width
of
binding

Fold in
end
pieces
and
paste

1½"

Name Here

Carnations for Mother's Day

Make tracings of the leaf, petals, and calyx. Cut out. Use them for patterns.

Gather each circle of petals into a cluster from the center up and twist to hold in place.

Use 5 clusters for each carnation.

Cover base of petal clusters with green calyx.

Insert leaf in stem at center so that the 2 ends will come from opposite sides of stems.

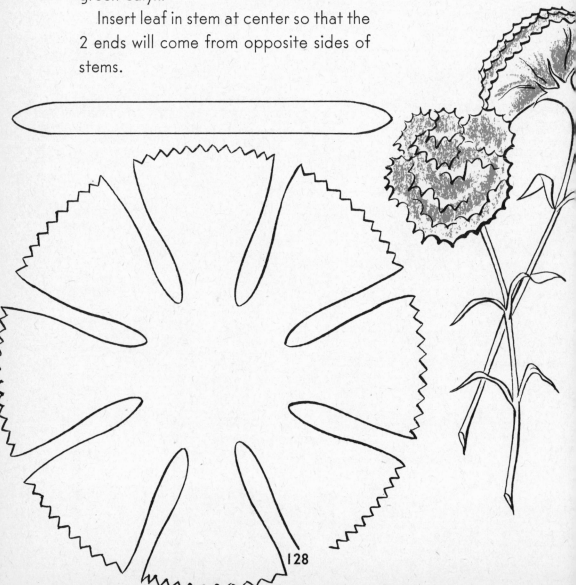

A WILD ROSE BASKET

Trace the pattern of the wild rose basket shown on this page onto a sheet of lightweight cardboard. With crayons color the centers of the roses yellow, the petals pink, the leaves green, and the stems a darker green. Then cut out along the heavy lines and fold on the dotted lines as shown in Fig. 1.

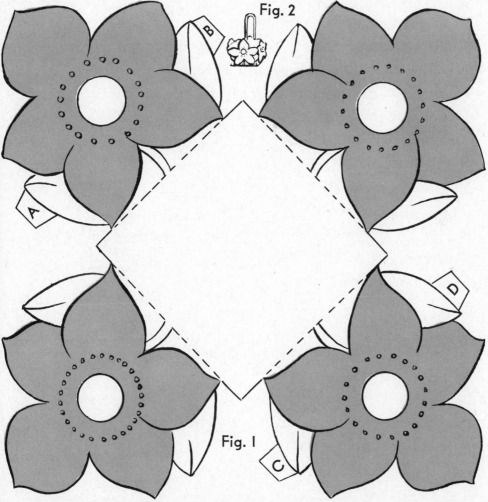

Fig. 2

Fig. 1

Use the tabs A, B, C, and D to paste the sides of the basket together. Cut out a handle, Fig. 2, paste it in place on the basket. Tie a small ribbon bow to the center of the handle. Fig. 2 (completed basket).

Tulip baskets may be made in the same way, using, of course, a pattern of a tulip instead of a wild rose.

A CLIPPING BOX FOLDER

A box folder may be used to hold drawings, pictures, or clippings. To make this simple box folder select a large sheet of tag or bristol board. Near the center of it draw a rectangle slightly larger than the clippings to be held in the box folder or file. Draw a second line all around the rectangle. Make the distance between the 2 rectangles the amount of thickness you wish for the file. Fig. 1. On 2 sides draw extensions measuring 2 or 3 inches in length (this length will depend on the size of the folder). Then extend the other 2 sides so that they will fold over to make the top. Cut as shown in Fig. 2. Decorate with pictures cut from magazines, or gift wrapping paper, or chintz. Then fold on dotted lines. Cut slits as seen in Fig. 2. Run a ribbon or cord through these slits. Tie in place.

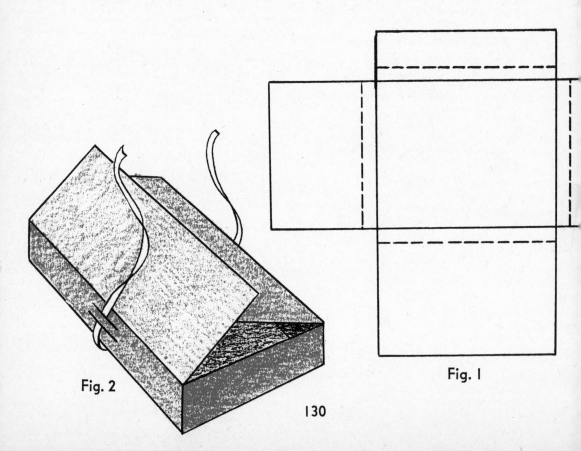

Fig. 2

Fig. 1

Box with a Cover

To construct a box with a cover use the diagram given on this page for a pattern. Be sure to fold on the dotted lines, cut on the heavy lines and put together as shown in Fig. 1.

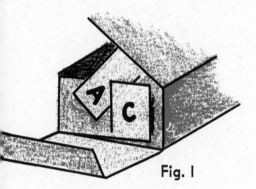

Fig. 1

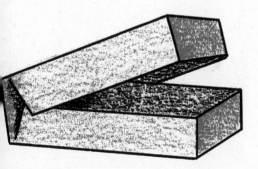

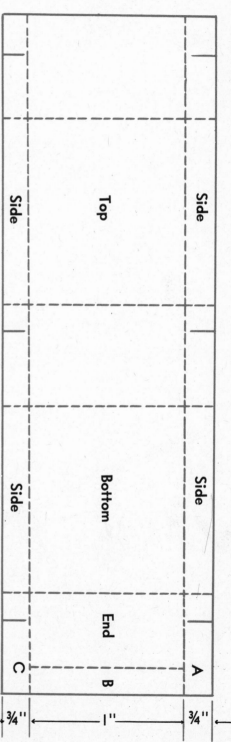

Kites are fun to make and more fun to fly. Notch, glue, and bind together the kite parts as shown in Figs. 1, 2. Lash notched ends, attach string to ends of crossbar to form bow as shown in Fig. 3. Then pass another string through 4 notched ends to form string frame. String tightly, Fig. 5.

Use light paper or fine cloth (starched) to make covering. Cut covering large enough to cover kite from top to bottom, and side to side. Allow a one inch border, Fig. 4. This border is needed to fasten covering securely to string frame. Paste edges of border, fold it over, and fasten it over string frame, Fig. 6.

Attach string bridle and flying string as shown in Fig. 7. Lengthen or shorten string until the kite flies well. Fasten a "tail" made of pieces of cloth tied to kite as shown in Fig. 6.

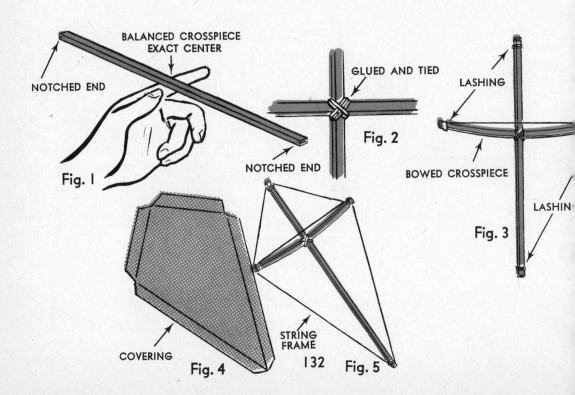

BALANCED CROSSPIECE
EXACT CENTER

NOTCHED END

Fig. 1

GLUED AND TIED

NOTCHED END

Fig. 2

LASHING

BOWED CROSSPIECE

LASHIN

Fig. 3

COVERING

Fig. 4

STRING
FRAME

132

Fig. 5

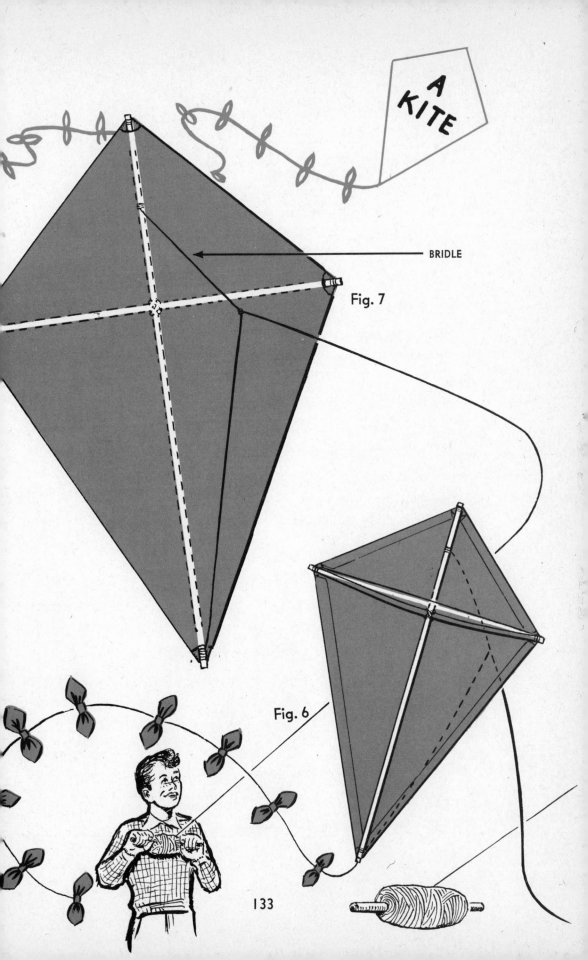

A KITE

BRIDLE

Fig. 7

Fig. 6

133

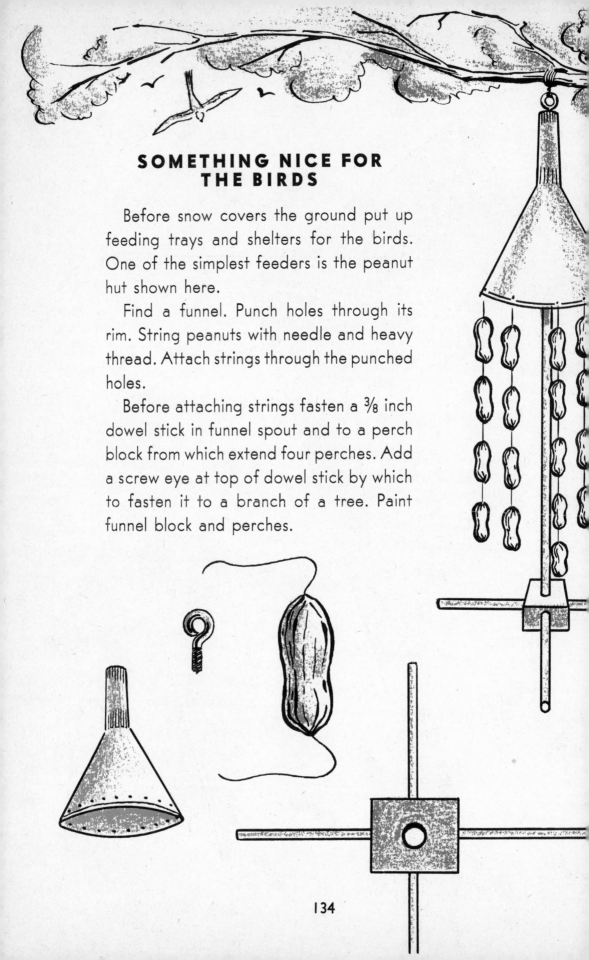

SOMETHING NICE FOR THE BIRDS

Before snow covers the ground put up feeding trays and shelters for the birds. One of the simplest feeders is the peanut hut shown here.

Find a funnel. Punch holes through its rim. String peanuts with needle and heavy thread. Attach strings through the punched holes.

Before attaching strings fasten a ⅜ inch dowel stick in funnel spout and to a perch block from which extend four perches. Add a screw eye at top of dowel stick by which to fasten it to a branch of a tree. Paint funnel block and perches.

Bird House and Feeding Station

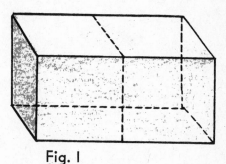

Fig. I

To make this combination house and feeding station obtain a grocery box that measures 2 feet in length. Draw 2 lines down the center of box. Fig. I. Remove ½ of each side. Fig. 2. Remove nails fastening the cut-out parts. Use a square piece of wood for roof. Nail in place. Fig. 3.

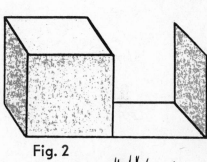

Fig. 2

Cut a hole I inch in diameter in front of house. Beneath this entrance fasten a perch. Nail house to a building or onto a post.

Use the roof of the house to hold a suet tree, a tin drinking cup, and seeds. A small railing around this room will prevent the seeds from being scattered by the wind.

Fig. 3

PAPER LANTERNS

Take a sheet of colored paper 9 inches and 6 inches wide and draw 2 lines ½ inch from each edge as shown in Fig. 1.

Then fold the paper in the middle lengthwise. Now cut the paper as shown by the dotted lines in Fig. 2. These lines measure ¼ of an inch apart. After all the cuts have been made, cut off the left-hand strip marked A in Fig. 2. Now open the paper. Fig. 3.

Put paste on the end tabs, marked B and C, and bend the cut paper to form a circle. Paste end tabs B and C to those marked D and E. When this has been done you will have a paper lantern like the one shown in Fig. 4. Add a handle to the lantern. It is then ready to be used for a Halloween, a Christmas tree, or garden party decoration.

If desired, a can cover may be used for a bottom to your paper lantern. This cover must fit exactly into the space at the bottom of the lantern, and be pasted or Scotch-taped into place.

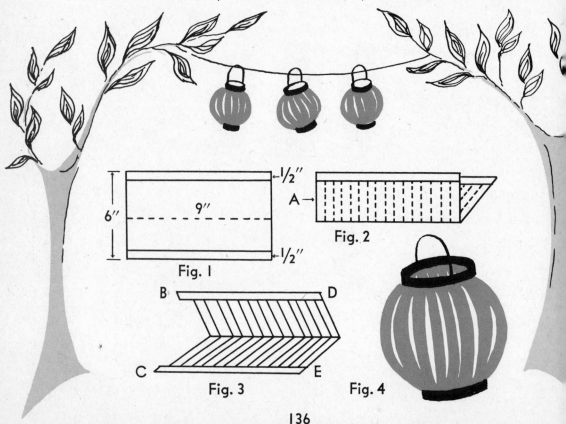

Fig. 1

Fig. 2

Fig. 3

Fig. 4

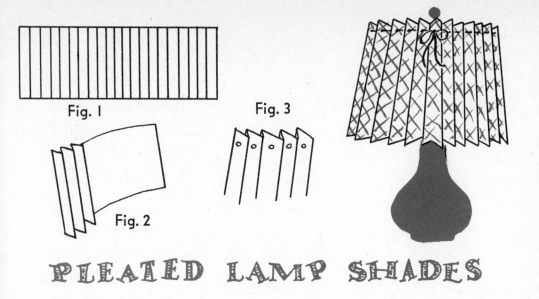

Fig. 1

Fig. 3

Fig. 2

PLEATED LAMP SHADES

Wall paper is an excellent paper to use when making a pleated paper lamp shade. Choose a pretty design.

The amount of paper to be used will vary with the sizes of the shades to be covered. But whatever the size, be sure to have the length 6 times the diameter of the bottom of the finished lamp shade. Thus if your lamp shade measures 8 inches in diameter at the bottom, you will need a piece of paper 48 inches long.

After the paper has been cut to the right length and width, take a ruler and pencil and mark off lines 1/2 inch apart. Fig. 1.

Join these points with very lightly drawn lines. Then start to pleat the paper. Each pleat should be 1/2 inch wide. The lines you have just drawn will be your pleating guide. Fig. 2.

When the pleating has been finished punch holes through the pleats. Fig. 3. Make holes 1 1/2 or 2 inches from top. Give the paper a light coat of pure linseed oil. Let the oil dry thoroughly.

When the paper is dry, glue the ends together and run a silk cord through the holes punched at the top. Fit the shade over your wire frame and draw the cord tight enough to gather in the top part of the pleats the correct amount. Then tie the cord ends to make a pretty bow.

A coat of clear shellac will help to make the shade keep its shape and it also will brighten the colors in the wall paper.

Spatter Pictures

Wherever spatter work is done be certain to protect clothes, walls, and furniture with newspapers or pieces of old oilcloth.

To make spatter pictures you will need an old toothbrush, a piece of window wire screen, ink, watercolors, show card paints, pins or thumbtacks, scissors, and white cardboard.

Cut a figure from a book jacket or magazine in the same manner as you would cut out a paper doll. Lay it on the white cardboard. Fasten securely with thumbtacks. Take a piece of screen and hold it about two inches above the cardboard. Then dip the toothbrush into the ink and rub it across the screen. This will send a fine spray of ink through the tiny openings of the screen and down upon the cut-out picture and the space about it. Fig. 1.

When the entire cardboard has been sprayed, remove the fastening and carefully remove the picture. You will be delighted with the silhouette production of the original picture and the shading about it. Fig. 2.

Colored dyes may be used in place of ink. Show card color produces the best results. This paint should be mixed to a thin consistency, but with no lessening of the color strength.

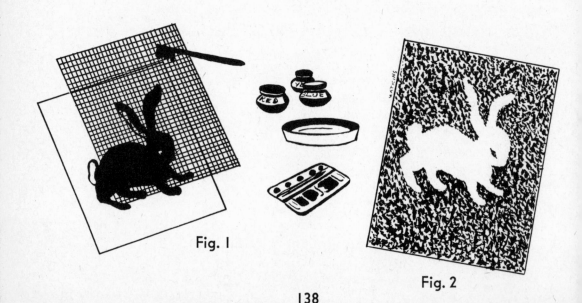

Fig. 1

Fig. 2

Harry Mane

A LION SOCK-PUPPET

To make this puppet, you will need a man's sock, size 10½, and red felt, a piece of flat sponge, 2 fat buttons, hemp rope, cardboard, needle and thread, brown tempera paint.

1. Turn sock wrong-side-out and sew tuck at heel. 2. Turn sock to right side and cut MOUTH. 3. Fold cardboard and cut wedge-shaped piece. 4. Pull sock onto one arm, insert cardboard. Pin sock over edges. 5. To line MOUTH, cut a doubled piece of felt to fit top and bottom. Sew sock and felt edges together. Add a tongue. 6. Cut a sponge NOSE and EARS. Sew them in place and paint them later. Fatten cheeks with cotton. 7. Sew button EYES above NOSE. 8. For the HAIR, cut 10-inch pieces of rope and separate the strands. Double and sew strands one at a time, around lower JAW and over HEAD. Sew a MANE down the back of the sock-NECK. Pull the puppet onto your arm. Open and close the MOUTH by moving fingers. HEAR THE LION ROAR!

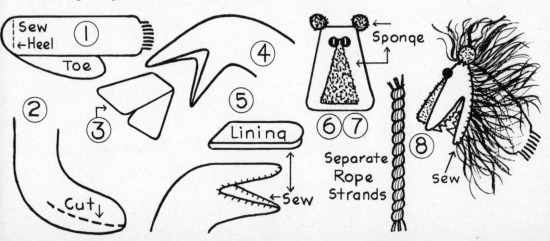

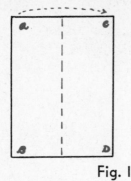

Fig. 1

A PAPER HAT

Obtain a sheet of paper **15** inches by 17 inches. Mark the Corners A and B and C and D. Fold on the dotted line as shown in Fig. 1. Then unfold.

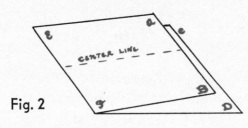

Fig. 2

CENTER LINE

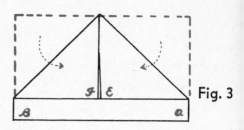

Fig. 3

Bring the edges AB to meet the edge CD. Mark the top of the fold E and F as seen in Fig. 2. Then bring corners E and F down until they meet at the center line. Fig. 3.

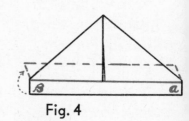

Fig. 4

Fig. 6

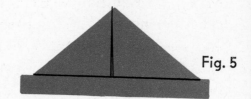

Fig. 5

Now bring the edge AB upward until it is touching the edges E and F. Crease into position. See Fig. 4. Turn the hat over and bring the edge CD upward so that it coincides with the new edge made by AB.

Fig. 5 shows a finished hat made according to these directions, and Fig. 6 shows how it can be worn by the maker.

Musical Glasses

Fill a glass with water. Tap it lightly with a spoon. You will discover it gives forth a musical sound. Then pour out some of the water. Note the difference in the musical sound.

Now arrange 8 glasses in a row on a table. Fill each with water at different levels and sound again. Notice how the pitch can be changed by adding to or reducing the amount of water in the glass. With a little experimenting you can line up the 8 glasses of water and play a scale on them. The key of G is a very good key to which the glasses may be tuned.

The tapper, a silver spoon, or a slender stick with a wooden ball at the end, and the kind of table upon which the glasses rest, will make a decided difference in obtaining the tones you desire to obtain from the glasses.

After you have the scale adjusted on the glasses, number them 1, 2, 3, 4, 5, 6, 7, and 8. This will make your playing a tune on them easier. Yes, you can play tunes on these glasses. Try it.

Drums

Fig. 1

Fig. 2

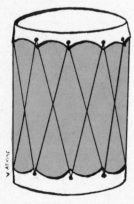

Fig. 3

There are two kinds of drums which boys and girls can make. One is a kettle drum and the other is a barrel drum.

To make a barrel drum you will need a hollow cylinder of some kind. A barrel or a keg may serve as the foundation. Each end must be covered with a skin.

The best covering for a drum is a skin called a "drumhead." It can be purchased in stores where musical instruments and music supplies are sold. It is an expensive material to use. Very strong paper or film cloth will serve the same purpose if the drum is not going to receive rough handling. One or two coats of shellac or varnish covering the cloth will make a better-toned drum.

Only one skin is needed for a kettle drum. A mixing bowl, a tin pail, or a wooden chopping bowl are a few of the things that can be made into a kettle drum.

The drumhead must be stretched tightly and held firmly in place. There are three ways in which it may be fastened to the body of the drum.

1. If the drum is of paper use thumbtacks. Fig. 1.

2. If there is a hoop around the drum body a strong cord may be wound tightly around the edge of the skin to hold it in place. A margin of an inch or more should be left for fastening the skins. Fig. 2.

3. The two skins may be held on the drum body by lacing a cord back and forth between them. Fig. 3.

Paint the drum body in your choice of color.

Obtain a box measuring 4 inches square and 1 inch in depth. Cut a hole and a slot in the cover. Fig. 1. Fashion a bridge from cardboard. Fig. 2. Make certain that the tab at the bottom of the bridge fits securely into the narrow slot, and that the bridge stands upright. Return cover to box and fasten with Scotch tape or gummed paper. Stretch rubber bands of various sizes over the entire box passing them over the bridge. The smaller bands which are stretched more tightly over the bridge will produce the highest tones. To play pick the bands with your fingers or a toothpick. Select simple tunes with which to begin your playing of the banjo; then go to work on the more difficult ones.

Select 2 blocks of wood about 1 inch by 2½ inches by 5 inches. Sandpaper them until they are smooth and all edges rounded.

Paint or shellac the blocks. When dry, sandpaper one of the 2 largest surfaces of each block. Measure and cut 2 pieces of sandpaper to fit these surfaces. Glue in place. When rubbed together, the sandpapered sides will produce a delightful shuffling sound.

a Rubber Band Banjo

Fig. 1

Fig. 2

Sand Blocks

a Tambourine

Cover an embroidery hoop or a box cover with unbleached muslin or heavy wrapping paper. Select 6 or 7 sleigh bells.

With a knife or scissors, cut as many slits in the rim of the box top as you have bells. Insert the bell hooks into the slits and fasten in place with the safety pins.

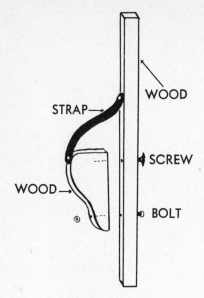

STRAP→   WOOD

WOOD→

→SCREW

BOLT

STILTS

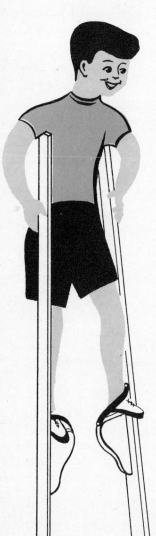

It's fun to walk on stilts. In learning to use them you may get a few falls. But if you start with a low pair these falls will not hurt. Stand on a chair with your back against a wall or tree. Place your feet in the stilts. Push forward and walk. You will soon learn how to keep your balance. Keep moving.

To make a pair of stilts you will need 2 strong sticks. The higher the steps are above the ground the stronger the sticks will have to be. The length of each stick should equal the distance of the steps from the ground plus the distance from the wearer's feet to his shoulders.

For the steps use 2 pieces of wood measuring 2″ x 4″ x 6″. Shape as seen in the sketch. Fasten them to stilts with a 3″ screw and 1/8″ bolt. Fasten a leather strap over each step to keep your feet from slipping off the steps.

A SKATE SAIL

To make a skate sail get 2 pieces of wood 7' long and 1" square. Bore a 1/4" hole centered 15" from one end of each stick. Sink square head of a 2 1/4" x 1/4" wing bolt flush with one side of frame. Fasten with a strip of tin. Fasten ends (at B) with a hinge. Cut a piece of wood 1" square and 5 1/4" long. Bore two 1/4" holes in it, centered 3/4" from each end. Attach one end to stick AB with the wing bolt. Attach the other end to stick CB with a 2 1/2" x 1/4" bolt. Use washers on this bolt between the pieces of wood and between the nut and wood. Fasten clothesline to two sides of frame 30" from B. Use it and strap D for hand grips.

Lay frame on a piece of canvas with stick D up. Mark frame and edge AC to the cloth. Allow 2 1/2" margin on sides at 1 1/2" at AC. Cut out canvas. Hem edge AC. Fasten canvas to sides AB and BC to top side of frame. To fold the sail remove wing bolt nut. Release end of D from bolt. Fold it down to B. Fold AB and BC together. Furl sail about the frame.

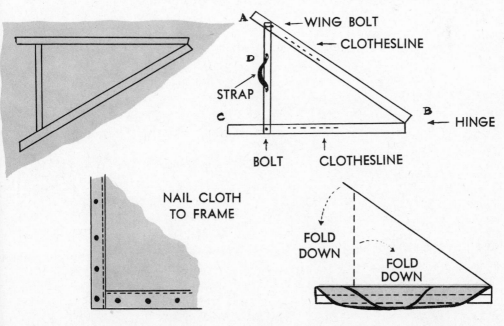

WING BOLT
CLOTHESLINE
STRAP
HINGE
BOLT   CLOTHESLINE

NAIL CLOTH
TO FRAME

FOLD
DOWN

FOLD
DOWN

A SKI POLE

A simple ski pole can be made from a broom handle. Cut it to measure 48 inches. Taper cut end into a point. Fig. 1.

Cut a 5 inch circle from wood $1/2$ inch in thickness. Bore a hole in the center large enough to slip the broom handle through it. Place this disk 6 inches from pointed end. Mark a line around the broom handle at the top and bottom of the circular disk. Fig. 2.

Drill a hole just above and just below the lines marked on the handle. These holes must be slightly smaller in diameter than the finishing nails to be driven through them and the hole for the second nail must be at a right angle to the first one. Figs. 3 & 4.

Drive in the first nail. Slip disk in place. Force it snugly against the wall. Then drive the second nail into the hole beneath the disk. Nails should be long enough to extend beyond handle. Fig. 5.

Add a hand strap made from an old leather belt. It must be made large enough to give the skier's wrist plenty of movement.

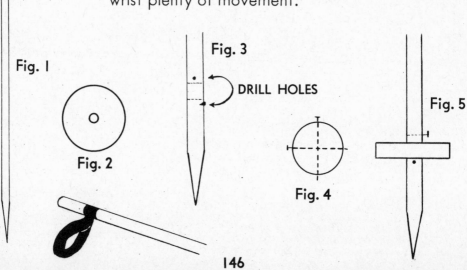

Fig. 1

Fig. 2

Fig. 3

DRILL HOLES

Fig. 4

Fig. 5

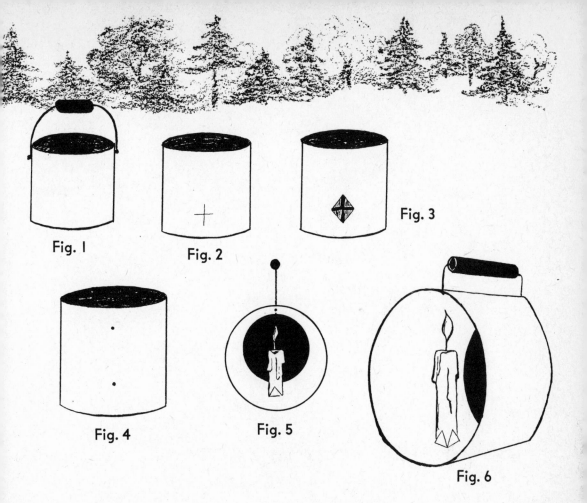

Fig. 1

Fig. 2

Fig. 3

Fig. 4

Fig. 5

Fig. 6

A CAMPER'S LANTERN

It's ever so much fun to make a camper's lantern. Just follow the directions given with these sketches and there's no danger of starting a fire with it.

Unhook the bail of a tin pail, such as a discarded syrup pail. Fig. 1.

Cut a cross on one side of the pail. Fig. 2.

Bend points inside of pail to make a holder for a cradle. Fig. 3.

On the opposite side of pail punch two holes. Attach the bail through these holes. Fig. 4.

Place a candle in the candle holder inside the pail. Fig. 5.

The camp lantern is ready for use. Fig. 6.

A WATER WHEEL

Fig. 1

Fig. 2

Fig. 3

Fig. 4

On these pages are sketches and directions to make two different types of water wheels.

The first is an overshot water wheel, so-called because the water is sluiced through a conduit and directed over the top of the wheel. Fig. 1. Note the angle at which the blades are set. This type of water wheel must have a lining of boards back of the blades in which to hold the water.

From boards with matched edges make 2 sides 3 feet in diameter. Fasten them together with cleats. Fig. 2. The 8" center cleat should be fastened securely in the manner shown in Fig. 2.

Make the blades 8" wide and 28" long. These should be held in place with steel wire nails driven through the round ends and into the ends of each blade. Cut a square hole in the center of each circular side through which to pass the axle, which may be

2½″ or 3″ square. Several inches from each side of the wheel give the axle a round shape so that it will revolve easily in the bearings which hold the wheel in place. Fig. 3.

A brook that has a short waterfall is an ideal place to mount a small overshot water wheel with a sluiceway to direct the water over it in the proper position. A pulley attached to the axle will provide the means of power transmission and a belt run up or across from this will operate a small piece of machinery.

When making a conduit always have the boards run in the same direction as the course of water. Bind them together with cleats placed 18″ apart. Prop up the sluice with strong planks and brace well for water is heavy and would soon tear the conduit away. Fig. 4.

The second water wheel can be made in the manner shown on page 149. It's yours for a couple of posts, an old cart wheel, an axle, and tin cans.

a silhouette portrait

Any clever boy or girl can cut a silhouette portrait, which is really a shadow outline picture.

Obtain a sheet of white paper. Fasten it on a flat wall. Then seat your model near it, and in a position that will permit you to obtain a good side view of his face. Now place an electric light, without a shade, in such a manner that it will throw a shadow of your model upon the paper. Then with a pencil draw around the outline of the shadow. Cut out around the outline. Place the silhouette on black paper. Trace around it and cut out. Then mount on a sheet of white paper.

a wooden loom

The frame upon which yarn is woven into cloth is called a loom.

To make a simple loom get a piece of wood measuring 8 inches by 4 inches. With a ruler and pencil mark spaces 1/4 inch apart at each end of the board. Notch at markings. The notchings must match. Fig. 1.

Wind thread around the loom. Arrange windings carefully at the notches so that the spaces between them are all the same width. Fasten the ends. These foundation threads are called warp threads. Fig. 2.

When the warp threads are ready choose a weaving thread to lace in and out between them. This weaving thread, called a weft, may be a strip of cloth, rug yarn, carpet warp or even string. Use a safety pin or a large darning needle for a shuttle. Start the shuttle under the first warp thread. Weave in and out until you reach the warp thread on the opposite side of the loom. For the second row turn the needle or shuttle around and go back across the warp threads in the opposite direction. Fig. 3. Continue in this manner until you reach the end of the weaving.

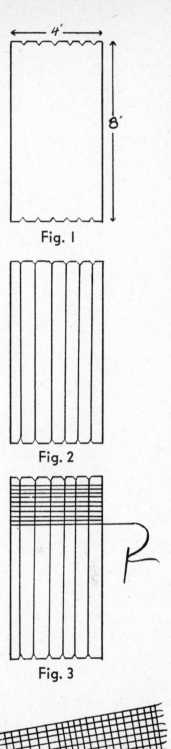

Fig. 1

Fig. 2

Fig. 3

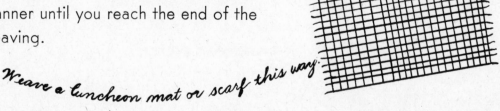

Weave a luncheon mat or scarf this way.

151

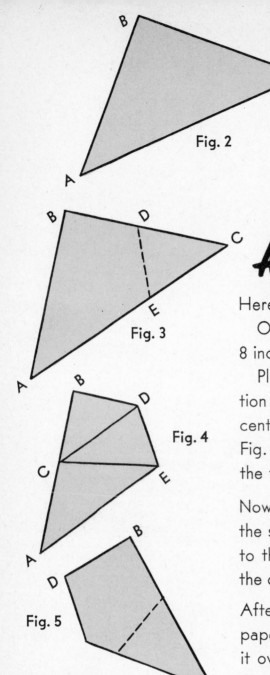

Fig. 2

Fig. 1

Fig. 3

Fig. 4

Fig. 5

Fig. 6

Fig. 7

A Paper Cup

Here is an easy way to make a paper cup.

Obtain a square of paper; 8 inches by 8 inches is a good size.

Place the square before you in the position shown in Fig. 1 and fold it through the center as indicated by the dotted line in Fig. 1. Your square of paper will now be in the form of a triangle. Fig. 2.

Now bring point C to the edge AB so that the section marked CD in Fig. 3 is parallel to that marked AE. Fold as indicated by the dotted line in this sketch.

After the folding process your square of paper will look like that in Fig. 4. Now turn it over to the other side and bring point A to D. Fold as indicated by the dotted line in Fig. 5.

Now bring upper sheet of point B downward on one side. Fig. 6. Turn cup over and repeat on the other side. Your paper is ready for use. Fig. 7. Note how the lower corners must be brought upward to keep the cup open.

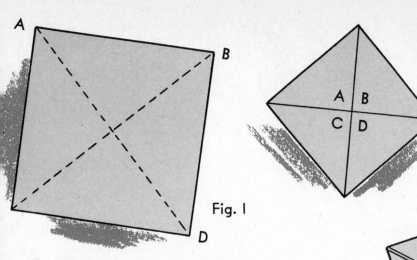

Fig. 1

Fig. 2

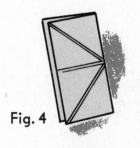

Fig. 3

A Sectional Flower Basket

To make a four sectioned flower basket obtain a sheet of firm paper at least 9 inches square and of the color that will be right for your flowers.

Fold the paper diagonally to find the center. Fig. 1. Open. Then fold each corner to the center. Fig. 2. Turn completely over and fold the corners of this side to the center. Fig. 3. Then fold the new square into a small square as indicated in Fig. 4. This done, unfold back to the last square. Fig. 5. Now open the loose corners. Punch a hole at the center folds. Run a ribbon through this hole. Tie loose ends in a bow. Fill each section with tiny flowers. Fig. 6.

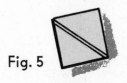

Fig. 4

Fig. 5

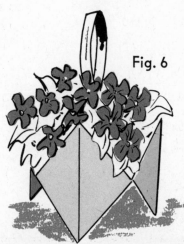

Fig. 6

153

Pad head of clothespin with cotton. Cover with white cloth or crepe paper. Add facial features with well-sharpened crayons. Sew yarn hair to head. Fig. 1.

Twist a pipe cleaner about clothespin to serve for arms. Fig. 2.

Insert between prongs of clothespin a folded piece of paper with feet cut out. Fig. 3.

Dress doll in a Bo-Peep costume.

If you wish to dress a clothespin doll to resemble a Halloween witch, use black and orange crepe paper to make the dress and cape.

Use string for hair. Clip loops to let the hair hang in single strands. Fig. 5.

To make a witch's hat follow these diagrams.

Paste sides of crown together, then paste notched edges of crown inside the brim.

BRIM

CROWN

CUT OUT

HOW TO MAKE A WITCH'S HAT

Dolls

Fig. 1

Fig. 2

Fig. 3

F

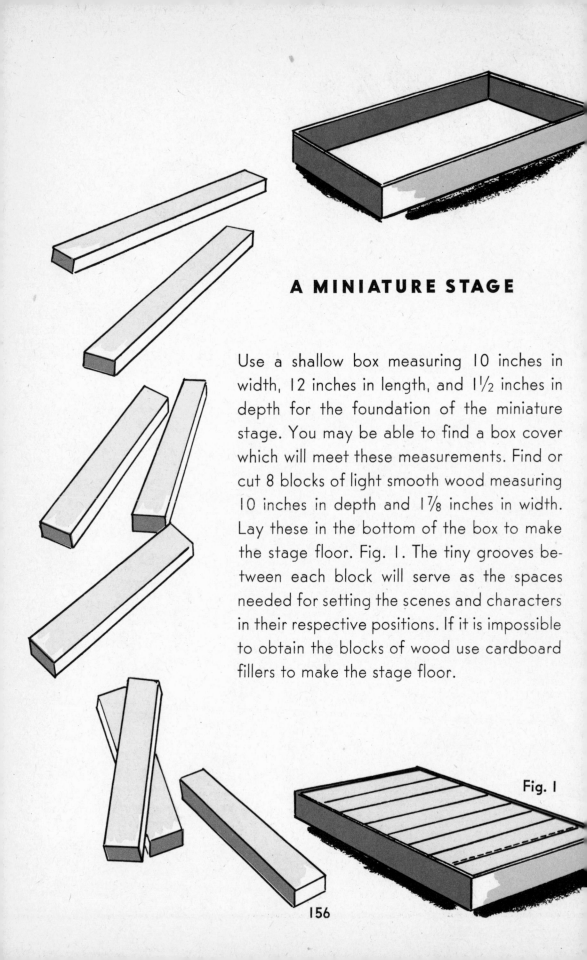

A MINIATURE STAGE

Use a shallow box measuring 10 inches in width, 12 inches in length, and 1½ inches in depth for the foundation of the miniature stage. You may be able to find a box cover which will meet these measurements. Find or cut 8 blocks of light smooth wood measuring 10 inches in depth and 1⅞ inches in width. Lay these in the bottom of the box to make the stage floor. Fig. 1. The tiny grooves between each block will serve as the spaces needed for setting the scenes and characters in their respective positions. If it is impossible to obtain the blocks of wood use cardboard fillers to make the stage floor.

Fig. 1

PASTE ON CARDBOARD AND CUT OUT

A SETTING FOR A MINIATURE STAGE

From an old story book cut out scenes and characters from a favorite story. Paste each picture on heavy cardboard and carefully cut, leaving a cardboard tab at the bottom of each figure or scene. Use the tabs to insert the cutouts between the grooves.

Insert the scenes and characters in the grooves according to their place on the scene to be enacted. In this scene from the story of "The Three Bears," the house is placed in the background and "The Three Bears" occupy the center of the stage.

TAB

157

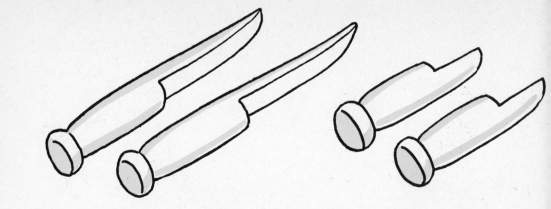

CLOTHESPIN DOLL CHAIR

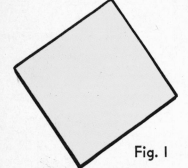

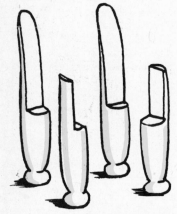

Fig. 1

Saw off the prongs of 2 clothespins 1 inch above the division point and one prong from each of 2 other clothespins. Use the first 2 clothespins for the front legs of the chair and the other 2 for the back legs. These 4 clothespins must be of the same length. Then cut from a piece of stiff paper a 2 x 2 inch square. Fig. 1. Use this for the seat of the chair. Glue in place. Fig. 2. Use 2 of the removed prongs to make the arms of the chair. Glue in place. Fig. 2.

Glue the other 2 removed prongs to make the chair a ladder-backed chair. Fig. 2. You may if you desire paint clothespins black, brown, or white.

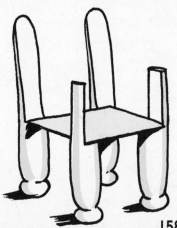

Fig. 2

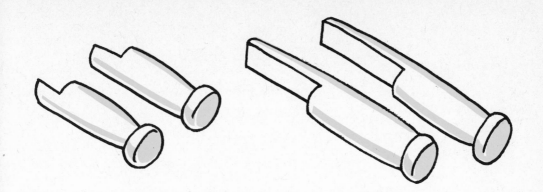

CLOTHESPIN DOLL BUFFET

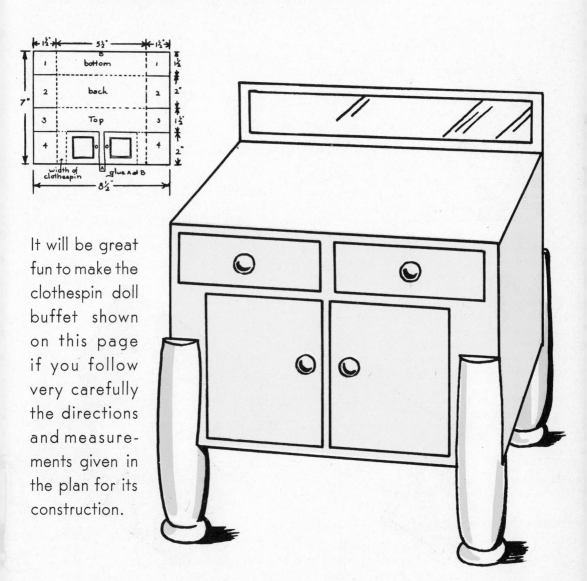

It will be great fun to make the clothespin doll buffet shown on this page if you follow very carefully the directions and measurements given in the plan for its construction.

Patchwork Fun

When our great grandmothers were little girls they spent many hours piecing blocks for quilts. Some of these blocks were simply squares cut from cloth, while others consisted of several sections put together to form a pretty design.

Let's create a quilt design from a square of wrapping paper. Fold the desired square or block several times as shown in Fig. I. Straight edges are always easier to cut and sew. Color sections of the folded square with crayon to create a design. See Fig. 2. Keep this for a guide. Then make an exact copy of your designed block. Cut it apart. Use sections as patterns from which to cut the various pieces of cloth needed to make your quilt block. Allow one-fourth inch all the way around each piece. Use this allowance to sew the block sections together. Be sure to consult the guide frequently during the sewing process. Make as many blocks as are needed to meet the measurements of your quilt.

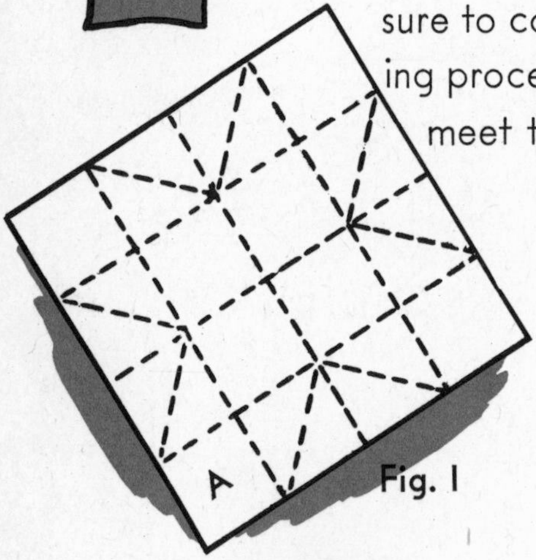

Fig. I

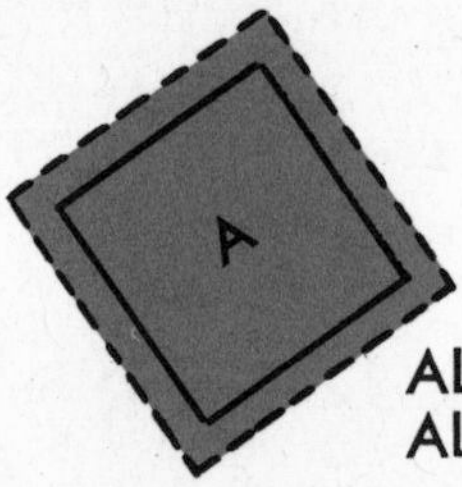

ALLOW ¼" TO
ALL PIECES FOR
SEAMS:

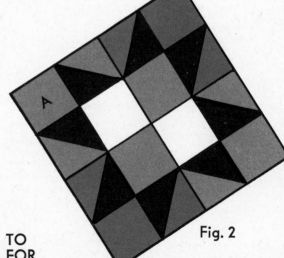

Fig. 2

A Hat Stand

Obtain a sheet of heavy paper which measures 15 inches by 15 inches. Mark the corners A, B, C, and D. Draw upon this square of paper a quarter circle as shown in Fig. 1. To do this tie a string to your pencil near its point. Then holding the other end of the string firmly in your hand at the point marked A, draw a circle like that shown at the bottom of Fig. 1. Start drawing from point B and end at point D.

Now measure up from point B 8½ inches. Fig. 1. Put an X there. Then with your pencil point at X and your left hand holding the string firmly at B draw the smaller circle seen at the top of Fig. 1.

Cut along the curved lines. Then join the 2 straight edges of the paper with paper fasteners. Before joining these edges, cover it with decorative paper, or if the stand is made from a pretty colored paper decorate it with cutouts of pretty flowers.

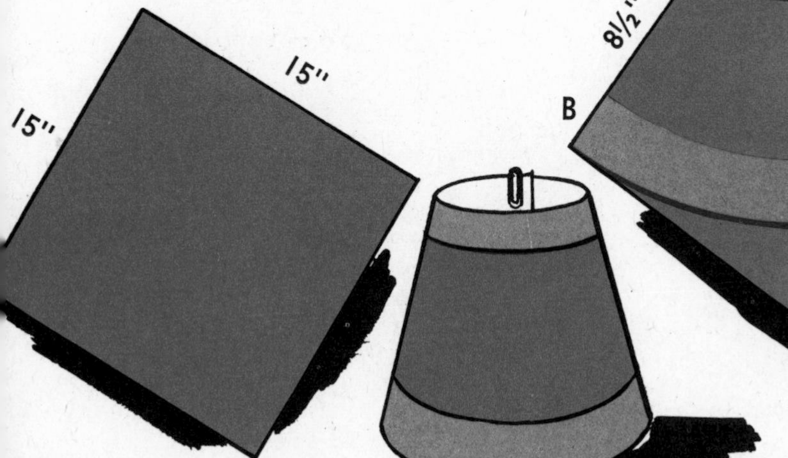

15"

15"

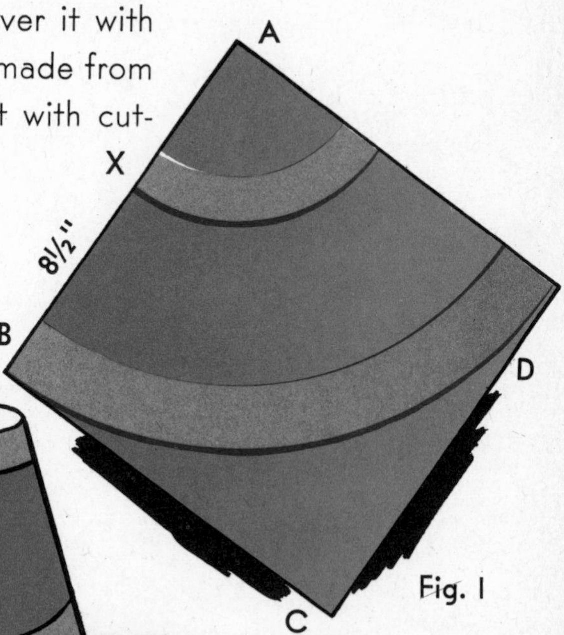

A

X

8½"

B

D

C

Fig. 1

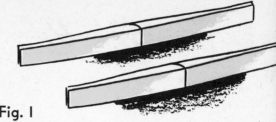

Fig. 1

CLOTHESPIN DOLL BED

Use 4 clothespins with prongs side down to make the Four-Poster bed. Cut 2 prongs $2\frac{1}{2}$ inches in length and two more 1 inch long. Glue these pieces together in the manner of Fig. 1. Repeat to make the 2 sides of the bed. Insert between the prongs of the clothespins, putting a dot of glue between the 4 posters to hold the side pieces. Fig. 2. Then make the head and foot pieces to fit the spaces between the head and foot posters. These should be fitted inside of the posters. Fig. 2.

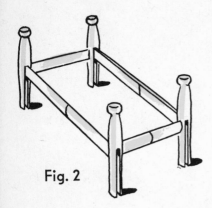

Fig. 2

To hold the mattress in place attach strings from end to end meeting the center. Fig. 3.

Make the mattress of 2 strips of cloth and stuff with cotton. Make the ruffled bed cover from calico or chintz.

Cut and fit together 2 clothespins to make the bolster foundation. Pad and cover with chintz. Fig. 4.

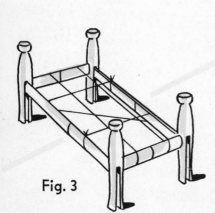

Fig. 3

Fig. 4

CLOTHESPIN DOLL COFFEE TABLE

Remove the prongs from 4 clothespins. Cut from lightweight cardboard the table top. Paste in place on the 4 clothespins in the manner shown in Fig. 1. You may if you desire paste a discarded mirror from mother's purse onto the table top.

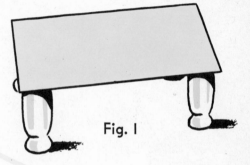

Fig. I

Fig. I

Fig. 2

CLOTHESPIN DOLL LAMP

Follow carefully the sketches given here and you will have an attractive lamp for your doll house.

Drawing for small lamp shade. Fig. 1.

Folded lamp shade. Fig. 2.

Cardboard for bottom and top of lamp stand. Fig. 3.

Completed lamp. Fig. 4.

GLUE

Fig. 3

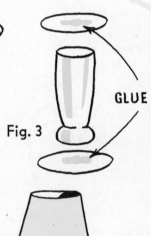

Fig. 4

Fig. 1

BUTTERFLIES-ON-THE-WING

To entertain your friends on a rainy afternoon, get a glass jar and a large cork to fit into its top. Fig. 1. Cut a hole in the center of the cork and fit a small funnel securely into it.

Cut several butterflies from tissue paper. Fig. 2. Glue a small bit of match stick to the center of each one.

Fill the jar about half full of water. Drop a package of Seidlitz powder into it. Close the jar with the cork. Place the butterflies inside the funnel.

When the Seidlitz powder begins to effervesce, the gas given off by this process will pass through the funnel and send the butterflies winging about the room.

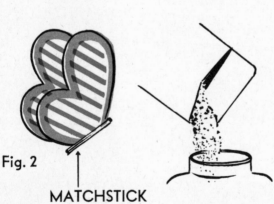

Fig. 2

MATCHSTICK

164

DOLLS FROM TWIGS

When autumn winds send the leaves fluttering here, there, and everywhere, the time has come for you to go forth in search of twigs that have something of the appearance of a person's form. Fig. I. With a supply of twigs at hand, cut faces, Fig. 2; hands, Fig. 3; feet, Fig. 4; from magazine pictures. Cut them double and then mount with glue on the twigs. Fig. 5. Now from pieces of cloth fashion dresses and suits to dress your twig dolls.

Fig. I

Fig. 3

Fig. 2

Fig. 4

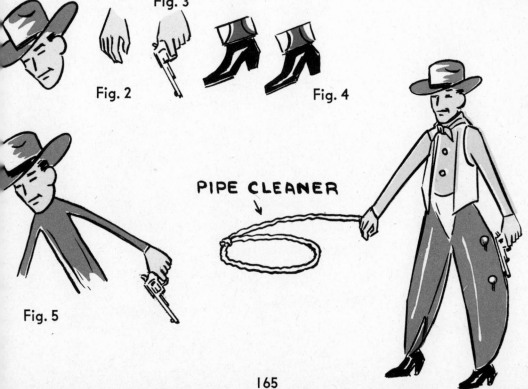

PIPE CLEANER

Fig. 5

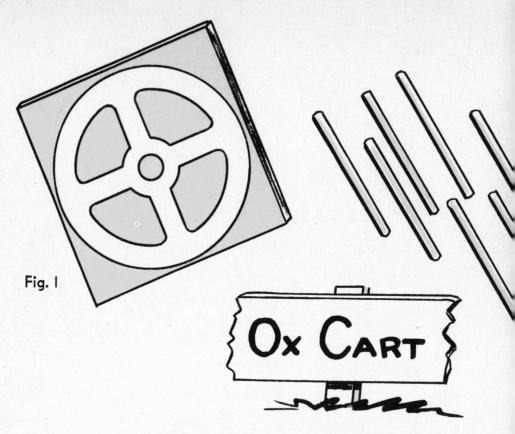

Fig. I

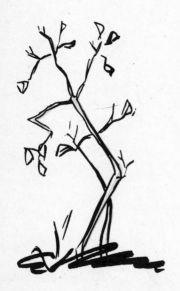

Ox Cart

For the boy or girl who likes to whittle there is nothing better than making an old-fashioned, two-wheeled ox cart. To make, trace and cut out the wheel pattern. Fig. I. Place it upon a piece of wood, trace, and cut out. Repeat to make second wheel.

Then cut a piece of wood to measure 7 inches by 4 inches and bore 12 holes in it to accommodate 12 sticks of wood. To these sticks attach 2 side pieces with cord or pieces of leather. Fig. 2.

Make tongue as shown. Attach it and the wheel to the cart as depicted herewith. Use a washer between each wheel and the axle.

Whittle from wood the figure of the ox. Harness it to the cart.

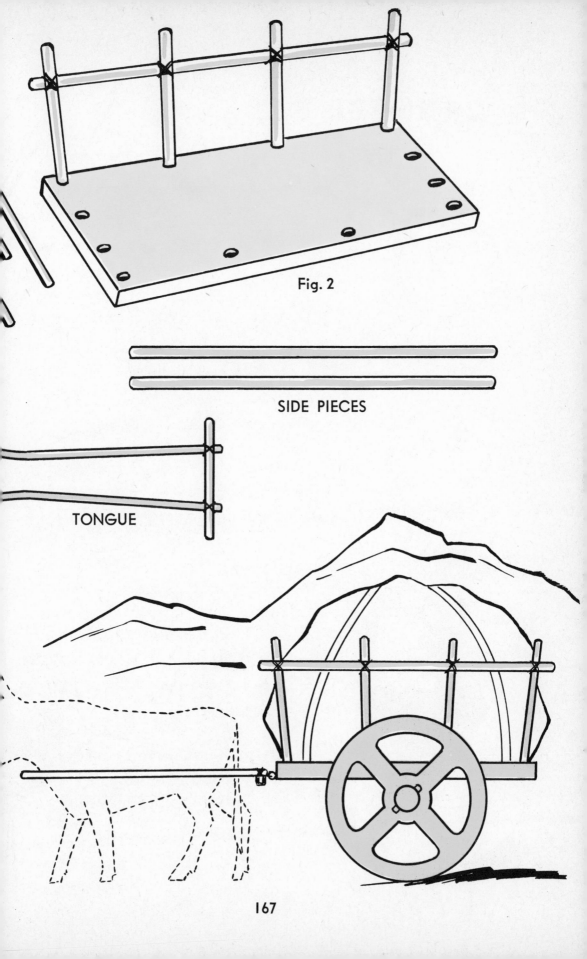

Fig. 2

SIDE PIECES

TONGUE

167

CRUMBER SET

Fig. I

Decorate a colored paper plate with flower designs cut from a flower catalogue or a magazine. Paste the flowers in place. Fig. I.

Now turn the plate over. With a pencil and a ruler draw lines on this side of the plate in the manner shown in Fig. 2. Cut along these lines. Throw away the small triangular pieces.

The remaining large sections will make the tray and the crumber of your crumber set. Shellac the set.

Fig. 2

INDIAN HEADBAND

From corrugated paper cut a strip 1½ inches wide and 2 inches longer than your head size. Into the holes of the paper stick feathers. Then cover the outside of the headband with a strip of bright red crepe paper 2 inches wide and long enough to make long streamers. Frill the edges of this strip of paper. Paste in place. Overlap ends of corrugated headband. Punch a hole in each end. Slip a 2-pronged paper fastener through these holes and spread the prongs.

CORRUGATED PAPER

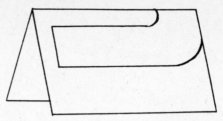

Fig. 1

Fig. 2

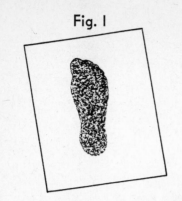

Fig. 3

INDIAN MOCCASINS

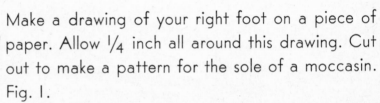

Make a drawing of your right foot on a piece of paper. Allow 1/4 inch all around this drawing. Cut out to make a pattern for the sole of a moccasin. Fig. 1.

Measure the distance around the outside of your pattern. Draw a U shaped figure that equals this measurement. Be sure that the width of the toe part of the U is 2 inches. Fig. 2.

When you are certain that these patterns are the correct size, place them on a piece of felt and cut around them.

With bright colored yarn overcast the two pieces together as shown in Fig. 3.

Then fit an oval-shaped "tongue" of the same felt into the front portion of the moccasin and overcast into place. Add a beaded design to the tongue.

To make the moccasin for the left foot reverse the sole pattern. Put together as you did the one for the right foot.

Crepe paper vegetable dolls make attractive decorations for a Thanksgiving Day Party.

Use a piece of wire twice the length desired for the doll, allowing enough for the feet. Bend and twist to form head and feet. Fig. 1.

Twist a second piece of wire around neck to make arms. Bend ends to form hands. If picture wire is used the ends can be separated to form fingers. Figs. 2 & 3.

Pad head, arms, legs, and body with cotton and cover with crepe paper. Paint in facial features.

From green crepe paper cut shapes in the form of spinach and lettuce leaves. Wrap these about the bodies of the wire dolls in the manner shown here to make spinach and lettuce vegetable dolls. Note how the legs of the spinach doll are bound together.

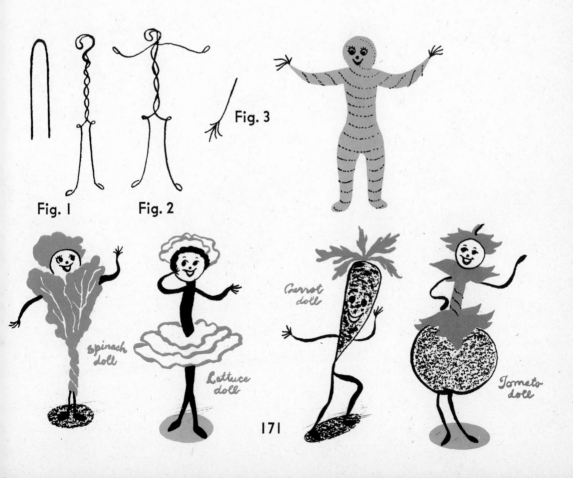

Fig. 3

Fig. 1   Fig. 2

Spinach doll

Lettuce doll

Carrot doll

Tomato doll

Make the framework of these dolls the same as you did for those described on the preceding page. It is only in the dressing of these dolls that there is any difference. In the case of the tomato doll the body must be padded and shaped to resemble a tomato before the body is covered with tomato-red crepe paper.

Note how the head and body of the carrot doll is made in one section.

Use a piece of heavy cardboard for a base upon which to stand each doll. Make 2 slits in each base through which to slip the wire feet of the vegetable dolls.

Carrot doll

Plum doll

Beet dog

Tomato doll

Cherry doll

PINWHEEL FUN

To make a pinwheel cut a piece of paper 4 inches square. Number the corners 1, 2, 3, and 4. Fig. 1. Join corners 1 and 3 and corners 2 and 4 with dotted lines. Then draw an X as shown in Fig. 2. Color each section, repeat the colors on the opposite side of the paper. Fig. 3.

Now cut along the dotted lines up to the X at the center of the paper. Then take corner 1 and lay it over the center. Place corner 2 on top of corner 1. Then put corner 3 on top of corner 2, and corner 4 on top of corner 3. Push a pin through all the corners and into the top of lollipop stick.

Hold your pinwheel against the wind. It will spin.

Fig. 1

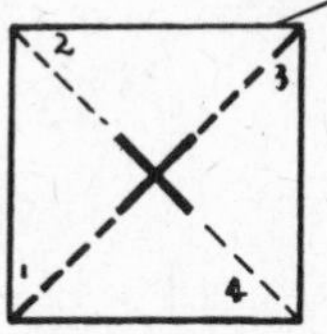

Fig. 2

Fig. 3

FUN WITH CIRCLES AND HALF-CIRCLES

All the figures on this and the following page have been made from circles and parts of circles.

Before starting to make copies of these figures, which will be great fun, get together a supply of circles. These can be made by tracing the tops of glasses, round buttons, round can covers and the like.

After you have created figures like these, try making others. Such figures may be used to decorate boxes, posters, and booklet covers.

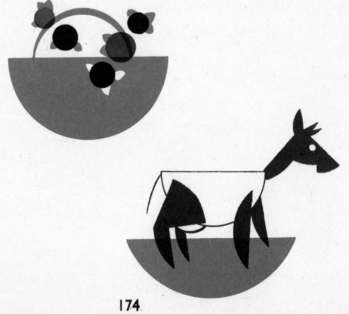

175

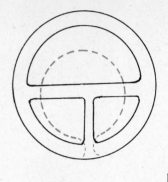
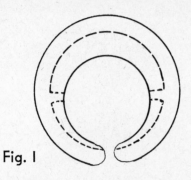

Fig. 1

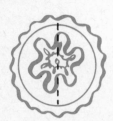

A PAPER PLATE HAT

Select a divided paper plate 10½ inches in diameter. Cut away a portion of the plate in the manner shown by the heavy dotted lines in Fig. 1.

Select 3 five inch pink lace paper doilies. Cut each in half. Use 5 of the halves to trim the hat. Fig. 2. Use Scotch tape to fasten in place.

At the center of the hat brim fasten a 7 inch light green doily, cutting away the section not needed.

Punch 2 holes in the back of hat. Fig. 3. Run a ribbon through these holes and tie in a bow.

Fig. 2

Fig. 3

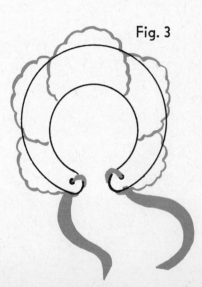

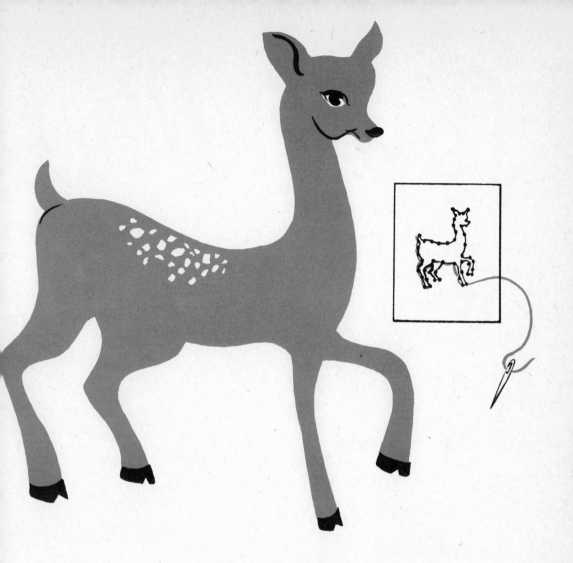

FUN WITH A PUNCH

Trace the outline of a deer or some other animal onto a piece of light cardboard. Color the deer light brown. Then with a pencil make a series of dots along the outline of the animal. Use a punch to make a hole at each dot.

Then with a large needle and dark brown yarn weave in and out among the dots to make a pretty yarn outline around the colored picture of the deer.

Papier Mâché

Fig. 1 ROLL NEWSPAPER TO FORM BODY

Fig. 2

BIND ROLLS WITH STRING

Fig. 3

COVER THE FORM WITH PAPIER MACHE

Fig. 4

TO MAKE ANIMAL SMOOTH PAT WHILE MACHE IS STILL WET

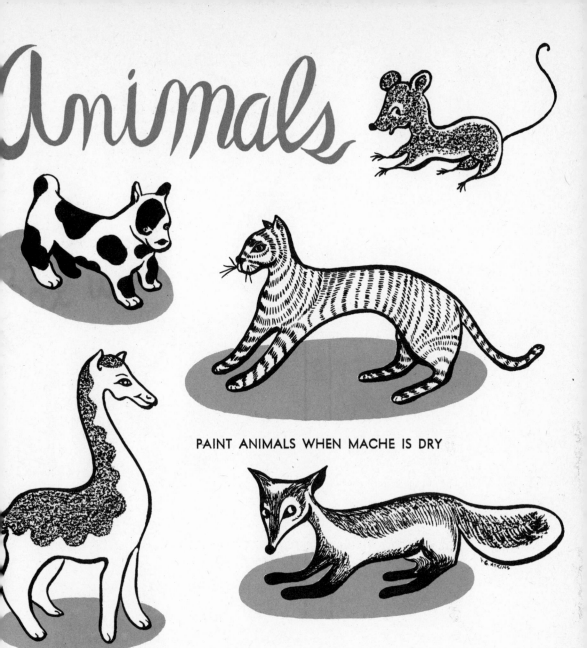

Animals

PAINT ANIMALS WHEN MACHE IS DRY

It's great fun to make papier-maché animals. Just follow the directions given on this page.

To make the papier-maché for these animals use shredded pieces of newspapers soaked and mixed with school paste to make it adhesive, or you may use equal parts of kalsomine and powdered clay mixed with twice as much water to which is added enough shredded tissue paper to make a modeling paste.

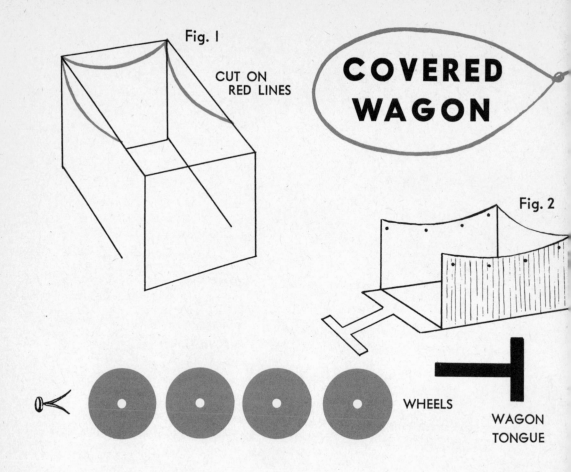

Fig. 1

CUT ON
RED LINES

COVERED
WAGON

Fig. 2

WHEELS

WAGON
TONGUE

Obtain a strong cardboard box. Cut sides down as in Fig. 1.

Punch holes at the top of sides. Fig. 2.

Cut a slit in front. Insert wagon tongue in this slit. Fig. 2.

Cut from heavy cardboard 4 circles of the same size. Attach these to the wagon box with two-pronged paper fasteners. Fig. 3.

Fasten pipe cleaners in the holes of the wagon to form the center framework for the white cloth. Fig. 3.

Cut a strip of white cloth the length of the wagon plus 2 inches and wide enough to reach over the framework and to provide for a $\frac{1}{2}$ inch hem on each side. Fig. 4.

Pass a pipestem through the hemmed ends. Fig. 4. Attach cover as shown in Fig. 5.

Cut a cardboard seat to fit in the wagon. Place pipecleaner dolls in the wagon headed Oregon way.

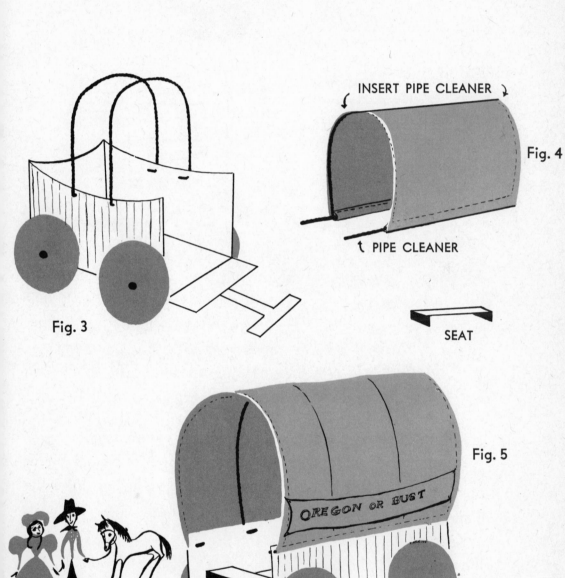

INSERT PIPE CLEANER

Fig. 4

PIPE CLEANER

Fig. 3

SEAT

OREGON OR BUST

Fig. 5

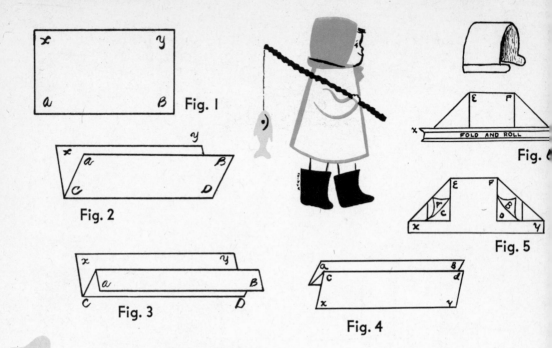

Fig. I

Fig. 2

Fig. 3

Fig. 4

Fig. 5

Fig. 6

FISHERMAN'S HOOD

To make a New England fisherman's hood, spread on a flat surface before you a piece of cloth, preferably woolen, measuring ⅔ or ¾ of a yard. Mark the lower corners A and B. Hold these corners until the hood is finished. Mark the upper corners X and Y. Fig. I. Fold the corners A and B up to meet corners X and Y. Fig. 2. Then bring down A and B to meet at C and D. Fig. 3.

Turn the material completely over, laying it down the other side up. Fig. 4. Then still keeping hold of corners A and C and B and D turn down in a triangle toward the center. The lower edge of the fold should be parallel to X and Y, and the lines A C — E and B D — F should be vertical. Fig. 5.

Keeping your fingers at AC and BD, use the thumbs to pick up the edge XY and roll it 3 or 4 times as shown in Fig. 6. Then still holding onto the corners (to prevent a turning of the hood upside down) place it on your head and tie the ends under your chin.

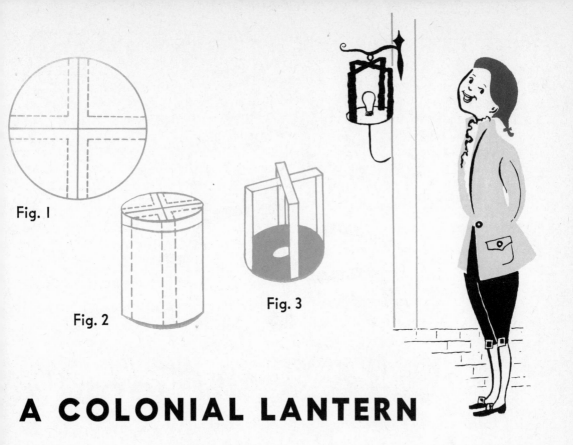

Fig. 1

Fig. 2

Fig. 3

A COLONIAL LANTERN

Obtain a round oatmeal box. Remove its lid, and draw 2 diameters upon it as shown in Fig. 1. Then draw lines parallel to the 2 diameters $\frac{1}{2}$ inch from either side, see dotted lines. Fig. 1.

Return lid to box, and extend the parallel lines drawn on it down the sides of the box to within $1\frac{1}{4}$ inches of the bottom. Fig. 2.

Use a scissors and cut cardboard away between the bars on lid top and between those on the box. Fig. 3.

Cut a round hole in the bottom of box. This should be large enough to insert the screw-end of an electric light bulb. Cover the inside and outside of the lantern with a thick coating of plastic wood. This can be purchased at a dime store or in a store that sells painter's supplies. Do not spread this coating smoothly if you wish your lantern to have an antique look.

Paint the lantern block after the plastic coating has dried thoroughly. When the paint is dry hang this lantern from a bracket as shown in the picture at the top of this page.

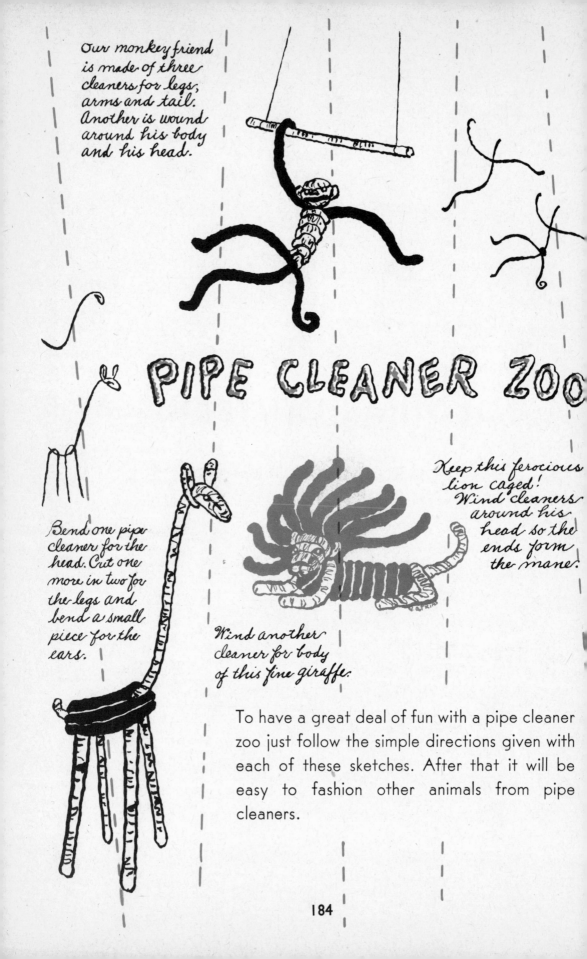

Our monkey friend is made of three cleaners for legs, arms and tail. Another is wound around his body and his head.

PIPE CLEANER ZOO

Bend one pipe cleaner for the head. Cut one more in two for the legs and bend a small piece for the ears.

Wind another cleaner for body of this fine giraffe.

Keep this ferocious lion caged! Wind cleaners around his head so the ends form the mane.

To have a great deal of fun with a pipe cleaner zoo just follow the simple directions given with each of these sketches. After that it will be easy to fashion other animals from pipe cleaners.

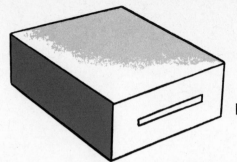

Fig. 1

JACK-IN-THE-BOX

Select a narrow rectangular box such as the type used to hold gelatin desserts. Remove the top flaps. Cover box with bright colored paper. Cut a slit in bottom of box. Fig. 1. This slit permits Jack to pop in and out of the box.

To make Jack, draw a circle 2 inches in diameter on white cardboard. Paint Jack's mouth, nose, eyes, ears, and hair in this circle. Fig. 2. Add a 4 inch neck to the circle. Cut out face and neck. Give Jack a gay colored ribbon tie.

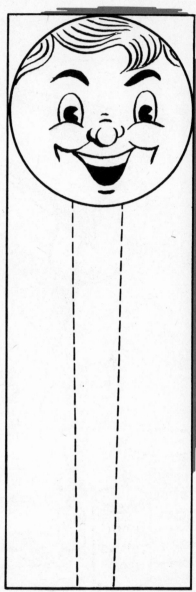

Fig. 2

Fig. 3

Slip Jack into the box. Then invite your friends to see him pop out of his box. Fig 3.

A ROCKET

EASY to MAKE

Large Oatmeal Box

Small Oatmeal Box

Glue

Tape

Heavy Cardboard for Fins

Light-weight Cardboard for cone

To make this rocket, obtain two oatmeal boxes, one large and one small. Tape covers on as shown in Fig. 1. Roll a cone from light cardboard to fit onto the small box, Fig. 2. Cut off the excess cardboard at bottom edge. Cut fins, 3 inches wide at bottom edge and tape them securely to cone, Fig. 3. Pour glue into cone head, Fig. 4, and drop in stones for weight. Let dry.

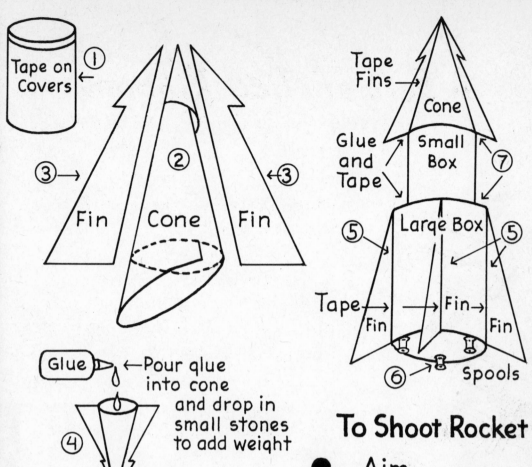

① Tape on Covers

② Fin — Cone — Fin

③ ← / →

④ Glue — ←Pour glue into cone and drop in small stones to add weight

Tape Fins →

Cone

Glue and Tape

Small Box

⑦

Large Box

⑤ ⑤

Tape → Fin

Fin →

Fin

⑥ → Spools

To Shoot Rocket

Aim

Thrust

Let Fly

Use plenty of arm force and shoot the rocket straight forward!

Cut fins, 4 inches wide at bottom edge to fit large box. Tape them securely to opposite sides of box, Fig. 5. Glue 3 spools to bottom, Fig. 6. When thoroughly dry, glue and tape cone to small box and small box to large box, Fig. 7. After tape and glue are completely dry, paint your rocket.

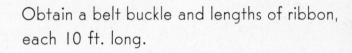

A Belt of Tied Ribbons

Here's the way to make a belt by tying knots in ribbon, raffia, or cord.

Obtain a belt buckle and lengths of ribbon, each 10 ft. long.

Double each length to make 2 strands.

Fasten each doubled ribbon to the buckle cross bar with a girth hitch.

Tie a knot in each pair of ribbons as near to the buckle bar as possible.

Do this with each of the 4 pairs of ribbons. This will make 4 knots in a row underneath the buckle bar.

NOW, TIE KNOT

Now proceed to tie knots in the strands of ribbons as shown here. Note how the rows of knots alternate between 4 and 3.

Continue tying knots in this way until the belt is long enough for its wearer. Then tie the 8 strands together in one large knot to slip through the buckle.

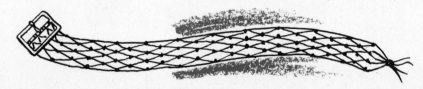

Hanging Vase

Select a flower pot or a glass jar in which you wish to place an ivy. Then cut 8 pieces of spool wire, raffia, or heavy string to measure in length 3 times the height of the jar or pot.

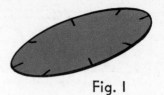

Fig. I

On a piece of cardboard trace the shape of the bottom of the receptacle. Cut the circle enlarging it a little more than the glass. Fold as in Fig. 1. Notch at each fold. Use this notched circle for a pattern. Place it on a thin piece of wood. Trace and cut out. Fig. 2. Make a small hole in the center.

Fig. 2

Thread one end of the 8 strands of wire or raffia or cord through the hole. Twist these ends together into a knot that will not slip through the hole.

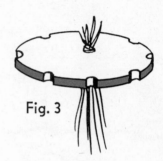

Fig. 3

Turn pot upside down. Place notched piece of wood on the bottom with knotted ends of thread against the pot. Fig. 3.

With a 1½ inch piece of cardboard measure down from bottom of glass and tie 2 neighboring threads together as in Fig. 5. Then with a 3 inch piece of cardboard measure the strands tie as in Fig. 5. Note diamond-shaped spaces created by this tying. Continue weaving in this manner to top of pot.

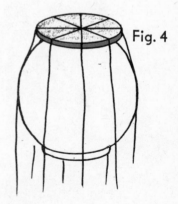

Fig. 4

Straighten the 8 strands and knot together at free ends. Hang vase from a hook. Fill pot with water and ivy.

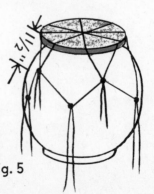

Fig. 5

BLOCKS

FROM WOOD

Select 2 ends from an orange crate. On one with pencil and ruler draw vertical lines running with the grain of the wood, 1 inch apart.

Starting with the fifth row, divide it and the next 3 rows in half horizontally. Divide the last 3 rows into 4 sections as shown in the diagram. Fig. 1.

Saw apart very, very carefully. Sandpaper, stain, and wax each block.

On the other draw vertical lines 2 inches apart and in the manner of Fig. 2.

Fig. 1   Fig. 2   Fig. 3

FROM CARDBOARD

From cardboard cut out a pattern of one side of a block which measures three inches by three inches. Trace around the pattern on a sheet of light weight cardboard to make a rectangle which is five squares long and three squares wide. Then cut out the rectangle and cut slits as shown in Fig. 1. Fold the rectangle into a cube. Fig. 2. Paste the slit sections to make the top and bottom of the cube. Color the blocks in gay colors.

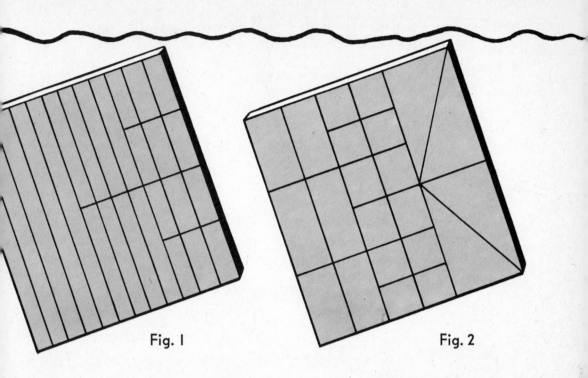

Fig. 1

Fig. 2

FROM OILCLOTH

Cut 6 five inch squares from oilcloth. Stitch together, leaving one side unstitched. Fig. 1. Fill with cotton. Fig. 2. Stitch unclosed side. These blocks may be made in various sizes and of different colors. Fig. 3. Little children will like them.

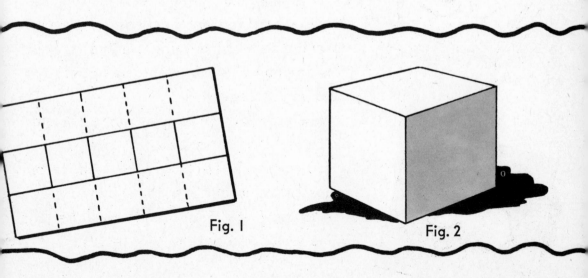

Fig. 1

Fig. 2

BLUE PRINTS

One of the most interesting and beautiful collections ever a child can make is a blue print collection of grasses, flowers, and leaves.

Blue paper is inexpensive when one considers the great number of pictures that can be made from a yard of it. This paper must be kept in a cool, dark, but not damp place. It should only be opened when ready to be used and then only in a semi-dark room.

To make a blue print of a flower, press the flower between layers of paper to flatten it and to remove any moisture. Then place it attractively on a piece of glass, or on the inside glass of a photograph printing frame. Carry to a darkened room.

Cut off a section of blue print paper the size of the piece of glass. Lay it, the inactive side down, over the flower. Cover with a thin piece of wood cut to the size of the glass, or if using the photograph printing frame, clamp down the back of the frame. See that no light gets through a crack in the sides between glass and the cover.

Now expose the blue print to the sunlight. Be careful that no shadow falls over the exposed·surface. The blue print whitens on exposure to sunlight. It will take a little practice to know how long a print should be left in the sunlight to get the best results.